OFFICIAL GUIDE TO BEANIE BAB

D0485156

TABLE OF CONTENTS

This is the 1st Edition of the Official Guide to Beanie Babies® Collector's Cards . Based on the enormous consumer response we received from the release of our 1st Edition Series I and Series II Collector's Cards, the Beanie Babies® Official Club™ deemed it necessary to compile this valuable resource to explain in thorough detail the excitement of collecting Beanie Babies® Collector's Cards and the thrill of *"the game"* that is interwoven through all existing subsets. We have taken great strides to insure the accuracy of our information and images so that this tool can be a valuable reference resource for the casual Beanie™ lover and the avid collector.

Introduction to Beanie Babies Official Collector's Cards

Hang on to your hats!

Welcome to the Ty Beanie Babies Official Collector's Cards Guide! Our goal is to help both the experienced and the first-time card collector find the most up-to-date, accurate information about Beanie Babies Collector's Cards, and have fun doing it!

First introduced in October, 1998, 1st Edition, Series I of the Beanie Babies Official Collector's Cards sold out in a mere three months, and collectors anxiously awaited the arrival of Series II. With the instant success of Series I, Beanie Babies card collectors have been asking questions and talking up a storm on web sites and in publications. Everyone wants to know how to get in the game!

Inside the Guide you'll find:

· The basics, such as what you should expect to see when you open a pack of Beanie Babies Collector's Cards, and how to get the most out of your collecting and trading experience. We'll show you how to "value" each card in your collection based on the four different categories of Beanie™ cards, and the color significance within each of those categories. If it sounds complicated, don't worry, we've made it easy!

· The official scoop on both Series I and Series II cards, including comprehensive, detailed information about Common cards, Birthday/Rookie cards, Retired cards, the Original 9 cards, and the Rare Bear cards. And, of course, the most sought after, one-of-a-kind cards: Ty Warner autographed cards!

· Pages of full-color pictures of each card in the 1st Edition. The Guide provides you with separate pages for organizing and cataloging all of the Series I and Series II cards. Each page provides space for recording when and where you purchased the card, the price paid, and the market value.

· The facts about why Beanie Babies Official Collector's Cards are so unique, and the best ways to care for them.

· Frequently asked questions and answers for Series I and Series II. Check this section out for ideas about how you can become more involved in Beanie card trading.

· A glossary of card terms that will help you become a more confident and knowledgeable collector.

· News on special releases and limited editions, such as Beanie Babies Official Club Kit — Platinum Edition cards and Series II for the United Kingdom and Canada.

Read on and enjoy the fun!

OFFICIAL GUIDE TO BEANIE BABIES COLLECTOR'S CARDS

It's All in How You Play the Game. . .

If you've never collected trading cards before, you may be wondering what all the fuss is about. After all, it's just a matter of luck, right? Not exactly. Collecting trading cards is a little bit like going on a treasure hunt with a good map and plenty of clues. There is some luck involved, but also a lot of calculation, which is what makes collecting and trading Beanie cards such a challenge. Most trading card manufacturers work off of the same general rules for production. Once you know the rules, you can use them to help you figure out the odds of obtaining certain cards.

There are usually several different levels of rarity in a series of cards, with fewer rare cards manufactured than common cards. A ratio of rare cards to common cards is established for the set that is produced. This ratio is then reflected in the individual packs of cards. Card wrappers will show the number of total cards in the set along with the odds of finding specific types of cards in one pack.

For example, the odds of finding a rare card over the entire production run may be indicated as 1 in every 7 packs. This gives the collector a ratio for the entire set, that the overall odds of finding a particular type of card is 1 in 7 packs. But there is no guarantee that out of every 7 individual packs purchased you will find 1 rare card. That's where luck comes in!

What's in There?

Common cards are the cards that make up the majority of every set, and, therefore, the majority of every pack. Chaser cards are the special, rare cards that are not part of the standard set of Common cards. They are called Chaser cards because collectors "chase" after them! Chaser cards are usually difficult to find since fewer numbers of them are printed and they are inserted randomly into packs in specific ratios. They come in a variety of types that may include holograms, foil cards, and embossed cards.

Each set of Beanie Babies Chaser cards is divided into four color categories, each with its own level of rarity. Part of the fun of collecting is in discovering an additional level of rarity that you may not have noticed right away!

What are the Odds of That Happening?

One of the challenges of finding and trading Beanie Babies Official Collector's Cards is trying to predict the odds for finding certain rare cards. So how did the Beanie Babies Official Club decide how many of each card to make? They based this number on many factors: In Series I, the rarity of that particular Beanie in the marketplace, the birth date and age of the Beanie, whether or not they are retired, and if the Beanie had low production numbers. So, in many ways, Beanie Babies Collector's Cards in Series I mirror the actual Beanie Babies themselves in terms of rarity and value.

Because we know how frustrating it can be to try to find one of those rare, elusive Beanie Babies, every now and then the Beanie Babies Official Club made some of the more rare Beanie Babies into easier-to-find Collector's Cards in Series II. The challenge for the collector is to try to figure out which ones!

Within both Series I and Series II, there are four basic categories of cards with varying degrees of rarity. In Series I those four categories, in order from least rare to most rare, are: The Common cards, The Birthday/Rookie cards, The Retired cards, and the Original 9 cards.

In Series II those four categories, in order from least rare to most rare, are: The Common cards, The Birthday/Rookie cards, The Retired cards, and the Rare Bear cards.

Within these four categories, there are additional degrees of rarity defined by levels of color and, in some cases, by crash-numbering, which is a numerical system that indicates that a card is one of a limited amount. Uncovering the many layers of rarity in a set of cards is part of what makes the trading game so challenging and fun. But, if you're a beginner, it can also seem complicated at times! In the following sections, we'll explain exactly what each of these categories and subsets are, and how to determine the level of rarity of each card in your collection.

1st Edition
Series I: 149 Different Cards in Set, 296 Total

What you'll find in each pack: 8 trading cards, 1 Beanie Babies Puzzle, Series I Checklist. The four basic categories of cards that make up the Series I set are: The Common cards, The Birthday/Rookie cards, The Retired cards, and The Original 9. Every card in the series is sequentially numbered, either on the front or back of the card.

Uncommonly beautiful. . .
The Common cards make up the majority of the Series I set. There are 100 Common cards, numbered 50 to 149. The front of each card shows a full-color, embossed (raised) picture of a Beanie against a scenic background. The name of the Beanie appears in large type in white on the background, along with the style number. On the back of each Common card

OFFICIAL GUIDE TO BEANIE BABIES COLLECTOR'S CARDS

you'll find: their birthday, issue date, the card number, and their poem. You will also see little-known facts about the animal or character that Beanie represents, written with assistance from the National Wildlife Federation® and Ranger Rick Magazine®.

Although the Common cards do not come with additional levels of foil, some are harder to find than others, just like with real Beanie Babies. The challenge for the collector is to try to figure out which cards are more rare — talk to your friends and stay tuned to the web to see which Common cards are appearing more often, and which are harder to find!

Now this is getting interesting. . .

The Birthday/Rookie cards celebrate the birthdays of different Beanies. If it has one, the Beanie's birth date is clearly shown on the front of these cards. There are 25 Birthday cards in Series I, numbered 25 to 49, and the odds of finding a Birthday card are 1 in 2 packs. The front of each Birthday card shows a full-color picture of the Beanie against a scenic background, with its birth date and sometimes a "Rookie" stamp. The back of the card shows the issue date, series number, and their poem.

Unlike the Common cards, the Birthday cards offer another level of rarity within this category. Each Beanie Birthday card depicts the Beanie's name on the front of the card stamped in colored foil. The color of the name determines the level of rarity of that particular card. There are four color levels in ascending order of rarity, with gold being the most rare: red, blue, solid silver, and solid gold. In addition, each gold level card is crash-numbered 1 of a limited amount, making certain numbers in the series more valuable. As with the real Beanie Babies, some Beanie Birthday cards are more difficult to find than others, which makes collecting and trading all the more challenging!

Show me the odds!

The odds of obtaining Series I Birthday cards:

 Combined odds: 1 in 2 packs
 Red level: 1 in 3 packs
 Blue level: 1 in 6 packs
 Silver level: 1 in 24 packs
 Gold level (crash-numbered): extremely rare

Things are heating up. . .

The Retired cards showcase a variety of retired Beanies. There are 15 Retired cards in Series I, numbered 10 to 24. Odds of finding a Retired card are 1 in 7 packs. The front of each Retired card shows a full-color picture of the Beanie on a holographic foil board background. The back of each card shows issue and retired dates, their poem, and a little-known fact. This category also offers different levels of rarity. The Beanie's retired date is shown on the front of these cards as a foil stamp. As with the Birthday cards, the color of this embossed stamp determines the level of rarity of that particular card. The following four ascending levels of color are used here: red, blue, silver, and gold, with gold being the most rare. In addition, each gold level card is crash-numbered 1 of a limited amount, making certain numbers in the series more valuable.

Show me the odds!
The odds of obtaining
Series I Retired cards:

Combined odds: 1 in 7 packs
Red level: 1 in 12 packs
Blue level: 1 in 24 packs
Silver level: 1 in 48 packs
Gold level (crash-numbered): extremely rare

What a find!

The rarest category of cards in Series I is the Original 9. This is the most challenging subset in the series. They are numbered 1 to 9, and feature the 9 original Beanie Babies printed on transparent acetate. The odds of finding an Original 9 card are 1 in 117 packs! The front of each Original 9 card is foil stamped with "Original 9". Again, it is the color of this foil stamp that determines the rarity of the individual card. The same four ascending levels of color are used here: red, blue, silver, and gold, with gold being the most rare. All levels of the cards in the Original 9 group have been crash-numbered 1 of a limited amount.

Original
9

Original
9

Original
9

Original
9

Show me the odds!
The odds of obtaining
Series I Original 9 cards:

Combined odds: 1 in 117
Red level: rare
Blue level: very rare
Silver level: extremely rare
Gold level: almost impossible

OFFICIAL GUIDE TO BEANIE BABIES COLLECTOR'S CARDS

One of a kind and tough to find. . .

Here's a treasure worth hunting for! The most difficult cards to find in the Series I collection are the cards signed by Ty Warner himself. One of each

of the 149 cards in the series has been signed in gold, including one each of the different color foil levels in the Birthday/Rookie cards, Retired cards, and the Original 9, bringing the total to 296 signed cards. Each of these cards is numbered in gold 1/1. These are sure to be the most sought-after and valuable cards in the series.

And did we also mention. . .

Each pack of Beanie Babies Collector's Cards also contains one of eight different Puzzle cards. Each of these cards is a colorful, two-sided mini-jigsaw puzzle. Puzzle cards are purely for fun and give Beanie fans a chance to see some of their favorite Beanies grouped together in different indoor and outdoor scenes. Puzzle cards have titles, including: Born to be Wild, It's a Dog's Life, Star Spangled Beanies, the Faces of Teddy, the Original 9, the Tropical

Heat Wave, and Winter Beanie Wonderland. There is an eighth untitled puzzle that depicts a tropical scene on one side, and Beanie Baby dogs on the other. Ty Warner's own dog, Cleo, is pictured hanging with the rest of the pack in this puzzle, and the tropical scene on the flip side is actually a photograph of a favorite vacation spot of Ty's — can you guess where it is?

In each Series I pack you'll also find a Collector's Cards Checklist. The checklist unfolds to show the name of every Beanie card in Series I, listed in alphabetical order, with a check mark box next to the name. The back of the checklist also shows some of the colorful, collectible Beanie Babies Official Club authentic products available for purchase.

If you buy Series I cards by the box, you'll get a free gift, also known as a "schmeggie" or "box topper" in trading card circles! In Series I, the schmeggie is a slider card that depicts some of the same scenes as the Puzzle cards, but on a larger, 5 x 7 card. The scene on the card appears in black and white until you pull the tab at the bottom of the card and it slides down to reveal the same scene in full color.

Series II: 151 Different Cards in Set, 304 Total

What you'll find in each pack: 8 trading cards, 1 Beanie Babies Trivia Game card, Series II Checklist. Every card in the series is numbered, either on the front or back of the card. The four basic categories of cards that make up the Series II set are: the Common cards, Birthday/Rookie cards, Retired cards, and The Rare Bear cards.

Now that we're all here. . .

As in Series I, the Common cards make up the majority of the Series II set. In fact, Series II Common cards are a continuation of Series I and are numbered 150 to 249 in the series. There are 100 cards in the series, each representing a Beanie not shown in Series I. Each card is beautifully embossed and printed in full color against a realistic, scenic background. Every now and then, the Beanie Babies Official Club made the more rare Beanie Babies into easier-to-find Collector's Cards. The challenge for the collector of Series II cards remains the same: talk to your friends and stay tuned to the web to see which Common cards are appearing more often, and which are harder to find!

Something borrowed, something new. . .

There are some similarities between the Series I and Series II Birthday cards, but some important changes as well! Like Series I, Birthday/Rookie cards in Series II celebrate the birthdays of 24 different Beanies. Some of the cards in this category are stamped "ROOKIE". These cards represent Beanies that were part of the "new release" of Beanies that came out after the introduction of Series I cards.

The Birthday cards are numbered 250 to 273 and the odds of finding one are 1 in 3 packs. But collectors of the Series I cards will notice that the Series II Birthday cards have an exciting new look. The cards are formatted vertically rather than horizontally, and each Beanie is depicted in full color on an etched foil background.

The back of the card features a new 'This Day in History' fact. The Beanie's birth date appears in gold foil at the top of the card, and its name is foil stamped below in one of four different color variations. As with Series I Birthday cards, these color variations determine the level of rarity of that particular card. There are four color levels in this series: blue, green, silver, and gold, with the easiest variation to find being blue, and the rarest gold. All gold level cards are also crash-numbered 1 of a limited amount, adding an additional level of collectibility.

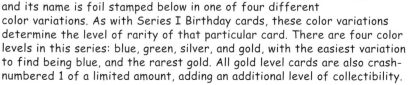

OFFICIAL GUIDE TO BEANIE BABIES COLLECTOR'S CARDS

Show me the odds!

The odds of obtaining Series II Birthday cards:

    Combined odds: 1 in 3 packs
    Blue level: 1 in 5 packs
    Green level: 1 in 10 packs
    Silver level: 1 in 30 packs
    Gold level (crash-numbered): extremely rare

If you're up to the challenge. . .

The Retired cards in Series II also showcase a variety of retired Beanies. There are 15 Retired cards in Series II, numbered 274 to 288. Odds of finding a Retired card are 1 in 5 packs. The front of each Retired card shows a full-color picture of the Beanie printed on a metallic holofoil board. As with the Birthday/Rookie cards, these Series II cards are designed on a vertical format rather than a horizontal one. The back of each card shows birth, issue and retired dates, and the poem. This category also offers a sub-level of

rarity. The Beanie's retired date is shown on the front of these cards as a foil stamp. As with the Birthday cards, the color of this foil stamp determines the level of rarity of that particular card. The same four ascending levels of color are used here: blue, green, silver, and gold, with gold being the most rare. Each gold level card is crash-numbered 1 of a limited amount, adding an additional level of collectibility.

Show me the odds!

The odds of obtaining Series II Retired cards:

    Combined odds: 1 in 5 packs
    Blue level: 1 in 8 packs
    Green level: 1 in 16 packs
    Silver level: 1 in 32 packs
    Gold level (crash-numbered): extremely rare

A rare bear indeed. . .

The rarest category of cards in Series II are the Rare Bear cards. There are 12 Rare Bear cards numbered 289 to 300, each featuring one of the

most collectible and rare Beanie Baby Bears made by Ty. The odds of finding a Rare Bear hologram card are 1 in 50 packs.

THE BEAR THE BEAR THE BEAR THE BEAR

The Rare Bear cards are stereogram holograms that produce an image of the bear that is rich in both color and depth. For the best color and detail these cards are best viewed under halogen light or direct sunlight. The front of each Rare Bear card shows the bear with its name and left chest emblem printed across the bottom of the card. Below the name, each card has been foil stamped for authenticity with the words "The Bear" in one of the four color variations for Series II: blue, green, silver, or gold, with gold being the most rare. All levels of the cards in this category have been crash-numbered 1 of a limited amount, adding an additional level of collectibility.

Show me the odds!
The odds of obtaining Series II Hologram cards:
    Combined odds: 1 in 50 packs
    Blue level: rare
    Green level: very rare
    Silver level: extremely rare
    Gold level: almost impossible

Once again, there's gold out there. . .
As with Series I, Ty Warner himself has signed one of each card type in Series II, creating a limited and very rare subset of 304 cards. These one-of-a-kind cards are signed in gold and numbered in gold 1/1. Happy hunting!

And that's not all. . .
Here's your chance to show off all that you know about Beanie Babies! Each pack of Series II Beanie Babies Collector's Cards also contains a Trivia Game card. There are twenty-five game cards altogether, and each has five Beanie Babies trivia questions and answers hidden beneath a scratch-off silver surface. Each question is worth a number of points, and the more questions you answer correctly, the more points you get! You can play the Trivia Game by yourself or with a friend, and there's even a special "tie breaker" circle at the bottom of each card.

In each pack you'll also find an updated checklist for the Series II Collector's Cards. The Series II "schmeggie" or "box-topper" that comes with the purchase of cards by the box is a two-sided, full-color poster depicting all of the cards in Series I and Series II. The poster is printed and varnished on each side, giving you the same high-quality graphics that you get with the cards themselves. The poster is a great reference tool for the collector, and a colorful addition to any room!

The Rarity Scale

The Rarity Scale is a tool for measuring the rarity of each card in Series I and II. It works like a sliding scale using three basic units of measurement: Difficult, Moderate, and Easy. Variations of color in between these units show different degrees of rarity. We've already assigned a color rating on the Rarity Scale to each card in the 1st Edition, based on the following breakdowns. Each bracket will show the general range of rarity for each type of card. Please see each card's individual Rarity Scale for a more specific rating.

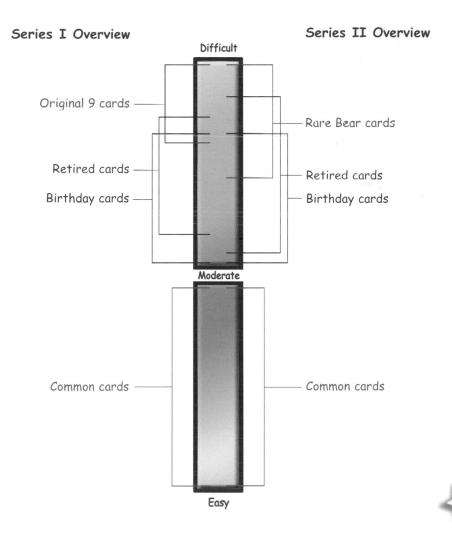

Series I Overview   **Series II Overview**

Difficult

Original 9 cards ————   ———— Rare Bear cards

Retired cards ————   ———— Retired cards

Birthday cards ————   ———— Birthday cards

Moderate

Common cards ————   ———— Common cards

Easy

A Word About Quality. . .

Beanie Babies collectors know what quality is. Beanie Babies Official Collector's Cards mirror the same quality and attention to detail that make Beanie Babies themselves so unique and valuable. The Beanie Babies Official Collector's Cards  in the 1st Edition stand head and shoulders above the majority of trading cards that you'll see on the market today. Why? Quality.

The Beanie Babies Official Club has ensured that each card in Series I and II, including the Common cards, meets a high standard of quality. This means trying to pack as much quality and value into each card as goes into each Beanie. We do this by using full color on every card, as well as embossing and varnishing techniques that make every Beanie look as close to the real thing as possible. The color and detail on all of the cards is sharp and clear. Innovative design techniques give the cards in the collection unique styles that reflect their level of rarity.

In the more rare categories of the 1st Edition, cards display designs such as foil stamps in a variety of colors, detailed etching, metallic holofoil board printing, and hologram printing. In addition to high-quality design, each card is packed with information about the individual Beanie, including little-known facts, birthday and issue dates, and series numbers. You just won't find the same quality in any other trading cards!

Handle with Care. . .

In order to ensure that all of the cards in your collection maintain the same "factory-perfect" look that you bought them in, we recommend lots of TLC: Tender Loving Care!

Mint: A card that is in perfect condition. A Mint card should be perfectly centered, have no defects in printing or coating, have sharp corners, and clear, vivid color. Mint cards have the appearance of a newly printed card. The age of a card does not determine its mint condition; a mint card does not have to be new, but must be in perfect condition.

Near Mint: A card that is almost perfect, or has only one or two very minor flaws or defects. These defects might include the card being slightly off-center, or having slight printing defects. Near Mint cards should still look like new, with no signs of wear or handling.

Excellent: This category is very close to the Near Mint category, but may show flaws that are due to handling rather than production, as with Near Mint cards.

OFFICIAL GUIDE TO BEANIE BABIES COLLECTOR'S CARDS

Very Good: A card that may show some minor wear and tear, but has not suffered any serious damage. Wear might include some rounded corners and a slightly off-center or out-of-focus picture.

Good: A card that has been handled a lot but is still in reasonably good condition. These cards may have some minor scuff marks and/or rounded corners, as well as some discoloration due to age.

Fair: A card that has several flaws that may include frayed or rounded edges, a fuzzy picture, or noticeable scuff marks.

Poor: Standard trading card term for a card that is noticeably damaged. Cards in poor condition may be creased, written on, or damaged in some other way.

All of the Beanie Babies Official Collector's Cards have some element of embossing or foil stamping, and many are hologram or holofoil cards. These design techniques are beautiful to look at and need special handling in order to protect them from smudges and fingerprints. We suggest that you treat them the same way you would treat a photograph: always have clean hands, hold them by their edges, and try to avoid directly touching the face of the card. Of course, part of the fun of collecting cards as unique and colorful as Beanie Babies Collector's Cards is showing them off to friends and fellow collectors. If you are handling the cards in your collection frequently for this reason, follow the suggestions above and try to treat them gently.

For both the serious collector and the more casual collector the best way to display and protect your collection is by using the accessories designed by the Beanie Babies Official Club specifically for use with Beanie Babies Collector's Cards.

> Official Collector's Card Display Album
> Official Collector's Card Storage Box
> Official Collector's Card Single Card Protectors
> (see pages 186 to 187 for details)

Good Care has its Rewards!

Trading card collectors use a number of standard terms to rate the condition of cards in a set. Whether you are assessing the value of your own cards or someone else's, these terms can help you decide their condition.

Experienced card collectors know that with every series of cards you can expect to see a certain amount of minor defects from the factory where the cards are produced. As with any manufactured product this damage is unavoidable and often undetectable at the factory (see FAQs in back of book). The most common damage found may be cracked foil, off-center images, or minor print defects.

COMMON CARDS

The Common Cards

For trading card collectors, the term "common cards" refers to the majority of cards that make up every pack in a set. These cards are usually easier to find than the subsets of rare "Chaser" cards. The 1st Edition Series I Common cards follow this same general rule; they make up the majority of the cards in the series and in each pack. But there is an important difference between the Common cards in this set, and those found in other trading card sets. There is not equal distribution of each of the Common cards. Unlike most trading cards, some Beanie Common cards are easier to find than others — just like the Beanie Babies themselves.

Another difference between the Beanie Common cards and other trading cards in the market is the design and production quality. The front of each Common card in Series I depicts a Beanie, the name of the Beanie, the Official Club logo, and a style number. The card is printed in full color, the detailed embossed Beanie gloss varnished, and the flat background matte varnished. The softly blurred natural scene in the background contrasts with the sharper embossed image of the Beanie to create an almost three-dimensional effect that makes it appear that the beanie is "popping" off of the card.

On the back of each Common card you'll find birthday and issue dates, along with the series number, little-known facts about the animal or character that Beanie represents, and the poem. There are 100 Common cards, numbered 50 to 149. These cards, although easy to moderately difficult to find, are a joy to handle and collect.

COMMON CARDS

Ally · 4032

Card #
50

Date Purchased: _____

Price Paid: _____

Market Value: _____

Purchased At: _____

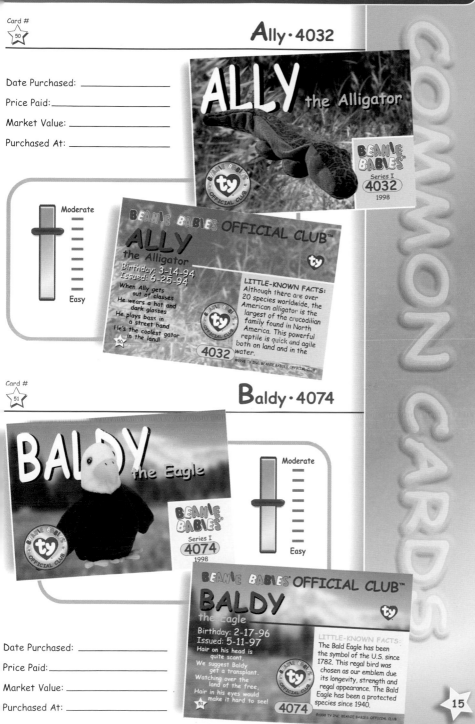

Moderate

Easy

ALLY the Alligator

BEANIE BABIES
Series I
4032
1998

BEANIE BABIES OFFICIAL CLUB™

ALLY
the Alligator

Birthday: 3-14-94
Issued: 6-25-94

When Ally gets
out of classes
He wears a hat and
dark glasses
He plays bass in
a street band
He's the coolest gator
in the land!
50

LITTLE-KNOWN FACTS:
Although there are over
20 species worldwide, the
American alligator is the
largest of the crocodilian
family found in North
America. This powerful
reptile is quick and agile
both on land and in the
water.

4032
©1998 TY INC. BEANIE BABIES OFFICIAL CLUB

Baldy · 4074

Card #
51

BALDY the Eagle

BEANIE BABIES
Series I
4074
1998

Moderate

Easy

BEANIE BABIES OFFICIAL CLUB™

BALDY
the Eagle

Birthday: 2-17-96
Issued: 5-11-97

Hair on his head is
quite scant.
We suggest Baldy
get a transplant.
Watching over the
land of the free,
Hair in his eyes would
make it hard to see!
51

LITTLE-KNOWN FACTS:
The Bald Eagle has been
the symbol of the U.S. since
1782. This regal bird was
chosen as our emblem due
its longevity, strength and
regal appearance. The Bald
Eagle has been a protected
species since 1940.

4074
©1998 TY INC. BEANIE BABIES OFFICIAL CLUB

Date Purchased: _____

Price Paid: _____

Market Value: _____

Purchased At: _____

15

1st Edition

COMMON CARDS

Bernie • 4109

BERNIE
the St. Bernard

BEANIE BABIES
Series I
4109
1998

Date Purchased: _____

Price Paid: _____

Market Value: _____

Purchased At: _____

BEANIE BABIES OFFICIAL CLUB™
BERNIE
the St.Bernard
Birthday: 10-3-96
Issued: 1-1-97
This little dog can't wait
to grow
To rescue people lost in
the snow
Don't let him out-keep
him on your shelf
He doesn't know how to
rescue himself!
52

LITTLE-KNOWN FACTS:
St. Bernards were originally
trained by monks to help
rescue lost travelers in
the Swiss Alps. They are
among the largest breed
of dogs - weighing over
170 lbs. when fully grown!

4109 ©1998 TY INC. BEANIE BABIES OFFICIAL CLUB

Moderate

Easy

Blackie • 4011

Moderate

Easy

BLACKIE
the Black Bear

BEANIE BABIES
Series I
4011
1998

BEANIE BABIES OFFICIAL CLUB™
BLACKIE
the Black Bear
Birthday: 7-15-94
Issued: 6-25-94
Living in a national park
He only played after dark
Then he met his friend
Cubbie
Now they play when it's
sunny
53

LITTLE-KNOWN FACTS:
Standing 4-6 feet in height
and weighing 100-350 lbs., the
Black Bear is actually one of
the smallest bear species
found in North America.
Black bears are well suited
for climbing trees, they
climb headfirst, but always
come down backwards!

4011 ©1998 TY INC. BEANIE BABIES OFFICIAL CLUB

Date Purchased: _____

Price Paid: _____

Market Value: _____

Purchased At: _____

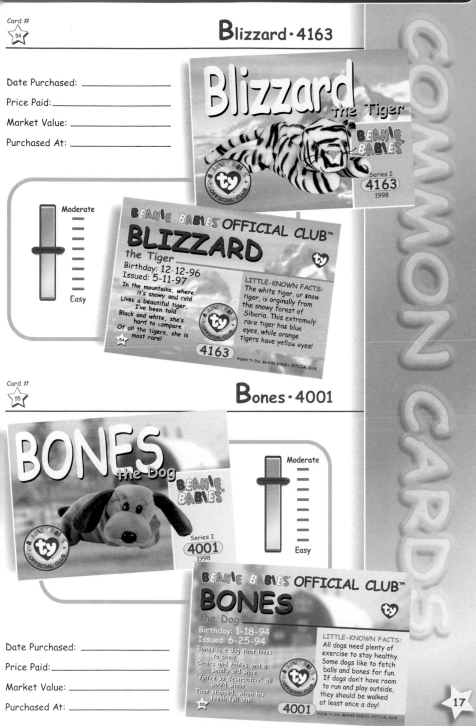

Card #
⭐ 54

Blizzard • 4163

Date Purchased: _____

Price Paid: _____

Market Value: _____

Purchased At: _____

Moderate
Easy

Blizzard the Tiger
BEANIE BABIES
Series I
4163
1998

BEANIE BABIES OFFICIAL CLUB™
BLIZZARD
the Tiger
Birthday: 12-12-96
Issued: 5-11-97
In the mountains, where
it's snowy and cold
Lives a beautiful tiger,
I've been told
Black and white, she's
hard to compare
Of all the tigers, she is
most rare!
54
4163
©1998 TY INC BEANIE BABIES OFFICIAL CLUB

LITTLE-KNOWN FACTS:
The white tiger, or snow
tiger, is orginally from
the snowy forest of
Siberia. This extremely
rare tiger has blue
eyes, while orange
tigers have yellow eyes!

Card #
⭐ 55

Bones • 4001

BONES the Dog
BEANIE BABIES
Series I
4001
1998

Moderate
Easy

BEANIE BABIES OFFICIAL CLUB™
BONES
the Dog
Birthday: 1-18-94
Issued: 6-25-94
Bones is a dog that loves
to chew
Chairs and tables and a
smelly old shoe
"You're so destructive" all
would shout
That stopped, when his
teeth fell out!
55
4001

LITTLE-KNOWN FACTS:
All dogs need plenty of
exercise to stay healthy.
Some dogs like to fetch
balls and bones for fun.
If dogs don't have room
to run and play outside,
they should be walked
at least once a day!
©1998 TY INC BEANIE BABIES OFFICIAL CLUB

Date Purchased: _____

Price Paid: _____

Market Value: _____

Purchased At: _____

COMMON CARDS

COMMON CARDS

Britannia • 4601

Card #
56

BRITANNIA the Bear

BEANIE BABIES
OFFICIAL CLUB TY

Series I
4601
1998

Date Purchased: _____

Price Paid: _____

Market Value: _____

Purchased At: _____

BEANIE BABIES OFFICIAL CLUB™
BRITANNIA
the Bear
Birthday: 12-15-97
Issued: 12-31-97
Britannia the bear will sail
the sea
So she can be with you
and me
She's always sure to
catch the tide
And wear the Union Jack
with pride.

LITTLE-KNOWN FACTS:
Britannia wears the
British Flag, also known
as the Union Jack, which
was adopted in 1801.
Great Britain's national
anthem is "God Save
the Queen" or "King,"
depending on who sits on
the throne.
©1998 TY INC. BEANIE BABIES OFFICIAL CLUB.

4601

Moderate

Easy

Bruno • 4183

Card #
57

Moderate

Easy

BRUNO the Dog

BEANIE BABIES
OFFICIAL CLUB TY

Series I
4183
1998

BEANIE BABIES OFFICIAL CLUB™
BRUNO
the Dog
Birthday: 9-9-97
Issued: 12-31-97
Bruno the dog thinks he's
a brute
But all the other Beanies'
think he's cute
He growls at his tail and
runs in a ring
And everyone says, "Oh,
how darling!"

LITTLE-KNOWN FACTS:
When dogs are young, they
are called puppies. Some
puppies can be very
attentive and active,
while others are very shy.
They're all different, just
like people!

4183
©1998 TY INC. BEANIE BABIES OFFICIAL CLUB

Date Purchased: _____

Price Paid: _____

Market Value: _____

Purchased At: _____

Card #
58

Bumble · 4045

Date Purchased: _____

Price Paid: _____

Market Value: _____

Purchased At: _____

Moderate

Easy

BEANIE BABIES OFFICIAL CLUB™

BUMBLE
the Bee

Birthday: Unknown
Issued: 6-3-95

Bumble the bee will not
sting you
It is only love that this
bee will bring you.
So don't be afraid to give
this bee a hug
Because Bumble the Bee
is a love-bug.

LITTLE-KNOWN FACTS:
Bumblebees live together
in large groups called
colonies. Bumblebees help
pollinate plants as they
move from flower to
flower, and they use
their long tongues to
reach nectar deep within
each flower.

4045
©1998 TY INC. BEANIE BABIES OFFICIAL CLUB

Card #
59

Caw · 4071

BEANIE BABIES OFFICIAL CLUB™

CAW
the Crow

Birthday: Unknown
Issued: 6-3-95

LITTLE-KNOWN FACTS:
Crows are known for their
agility in flight and their
intelligence. Members of
this species tend to
flock together in large
groups, and often nest
in the same site year
after year.

59

4071
©1998 TY INC. BEANIE BABIES OFFICIAL CLUB

Date Purchased: _____

Price Paid: _____

Market Value: _____

Purchased At: _____

COMMON CARDS

19

COMMON CARDS

Chip • 4121

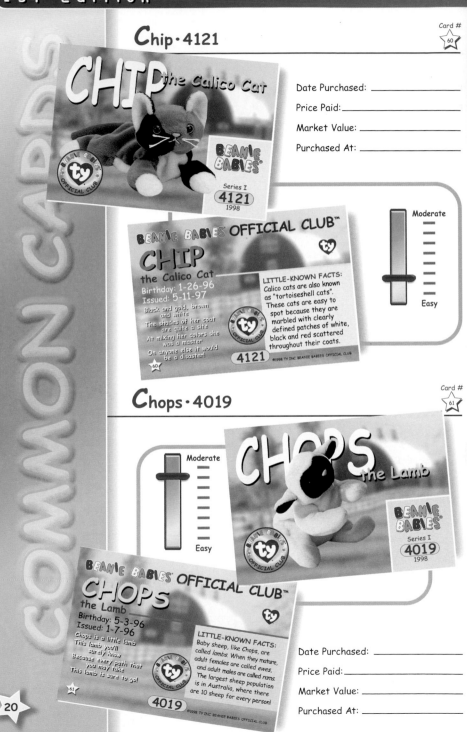

CHIP the Calico Cat

BEANIE BABIES OFFICIAL CLUB

Series I
4121
1998

Date Purchased: _____

Price Paid: _____

Market Value: _____

Purchased At: _____

BEANIE BABIES OFFICIAL CLUB™
CHIP
the Calico Cat
Birthday: 1-26-96
Issued: 5-11-97
Black and gold, brown and white
The shades of her coat are quite a site
At mixing her colors she was a master
On anyone else it would be a disaster!

60

LITTLE-KNOWN FACTS: Calico cats are also known as "tortoiseshell cats". These cats are easy to spot because they are marbled with clearly defined patches of white, black and red scattered throughout their coats.

4121   ©1998 TY INC BEANIE BABIES OFFICIAL CLUB

Moderate

Easy

Chops • 4019

Moderate

Easy

CHOPS the Lamb

BEANIE BABIES

Series I
4019
1998

BEANIE BABIES OFFICIAL CLUB™
CHOPS
the Lamb
Birthday: 5-3-96
Issued: 1-7-96
Chops is a little lamb
This lamb you'll surely know
Because every path that you may take
This lamb is sure to go!

61

LITTLE-KNOWN FACTS: Baby sheep, like Chops, are called lambs. When they mature, adult females are called ewes, and adult males are called rams. The largest sheep population is in Australia, where there are 10 sheep for every person!

4019   ©1998 TY INC BEANIE BABIES OFFICIAL CLUB

Date Purchased: _____

Price Paid: _____

Market Value: _____

Purchased At: _____

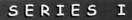

Card #
62

Claude • 4083

Date Purchased: _____

Price Paid: _____

Market Value: _____

Purchased At: _____

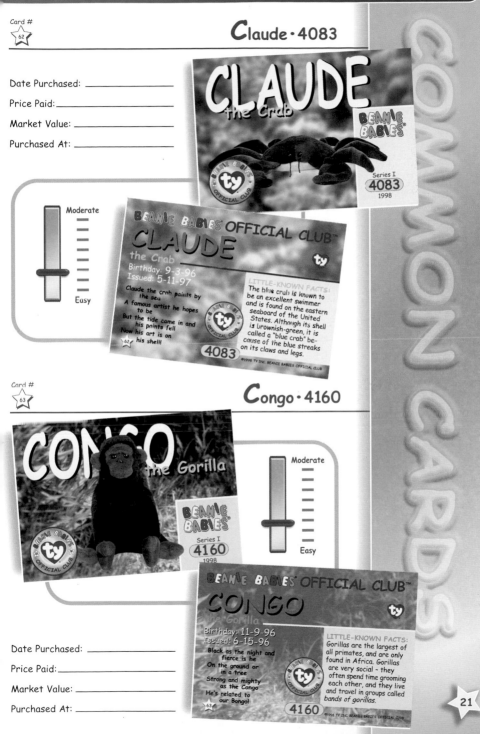

Card #
63

Congo • 4160

Date Purchased: _____

Price Paid: _____

Market Value: _____

Purchased At: _____

COMMON CARDS

Coral · 4079

CORAL
the Tropical Fish

BEANIE BABIES
Series I
4079
1998

Date Purchased: _____

Price Paid: _____

Market Value: _____

Purchased At: _____

BEANIE BABIES OFFICIAL CLUB™
CORAL
the Tropical Fish
Birthday: 3-2-95
Issued: 6-3-95
Coral is beautiful, as you know
Made of colors in the rainbow
Whether it's pink, yellow or blue
These colors were chosen just for you!

LITTLE-KNOWN FACTS:
There are over 600 different kinds of tropical fish. Our little "Coral" is named after tiny sea animals that grow together in groups, and look like giant, colorful plants in shallow parts of the ocean.

4079
©1998 TY INC. BEANIE BABIES OFFICIAL CLUB

Moderate

Easy

Curly · 4052

Moderate

Easy

CURLY
the Brown Bear

BEANIE BABIES
Series I
4052
1998

BEANIE BABIES OFFICIAL CLUB™
CURLY
the Brown Bear
Birthday: 4-12-96
Issued: 6-15-96
A bear so cute with hair that's Curly
You will love and want him surely
To this bear always be true
He will be a friend to you!

LITTLE-KNOWN FACTS:
The brown bear family includes the famous grizzly bear. This endangered species may be spotted in the Rockies, but rarely. They are more prominently seen in Alaska, northern Canada, and other areas of the Pacific Northwest.

4052
©1998 TY INC. BEANIE BABIES OFFICIAL CLUB

Date Purchased: _____

Price Paid: _____

Market Value: _____

Purchased At: _____

COMMON CARDS

Card #
66

Daisy • 4006

Date Purchased: _____

Price Paid: _____

Market Value: _____

Purchased At: _____

DAISY the Cow
BEANIE BABIES
Series I
4006
1998

Moderate

Easy

BEANIE BABIES OFFICIAL CLUB™
DAISY
the Cow
Birthday: 5-10-94
Issued: 6-25-94
Daisy drinks milk
each night
So her coat is shiny
and bright
Milk is good for your
hair and skin
What a way for your
day to begin!

LITTLE-KNOWN FACTS:
Cows are adult female
bovines. In the U.S., we
raise dairy cows for their
milk. This milk is used to
make many different
products, including butter,
cheese products and even
ice cream!

66

4006
©1998 TY INC BEANIE BABIES OFFICIAL CLUB

Card #
67

Derby • 4008

DERBY the Horse
BEANIE BABIES
Series I
4008
1998

Moderate

Easy

BEANIE BABIES OFFICIAL CLUB™
DERBY
the Horse
Birthday: 9-16-95
Issued: 12-15-97
All the other horses
used to tattle
Because Derby never
wore his saddle
He left the stables,
and the horses too
Just so Derby can be
with you!

LITTLE-KNOWN FACTS:
Baby horses are called foals
or ponies. Young males are
called colts and young
females are called fillies.
The smallest horse on
record stood 14 inches tall
and weighed only 20 lbs.
when he was born!

67

4008
©1998 TY INC BEANIE BABIES OFFICIAL CLUB

Date Purchased: _____

Price Paid: _____

Market Value: _____

Purchased At: _____

1st Edition

Digger • 4027

DIGGER
the Orange Crab

BEANIE BABIES

ty
OFFICIAL CLUB

Series I
4027
1998

Date Purchased: _____

Price Paid: _____

Market Value: _____

Purchased At: _____

BEANIE BABIES OFFICIAL CLUB™

DIGGER
the Orange Crab
Birthday: 8-23-95
Issued: 6-25-94

Digging in the sand and
walking sideways
That's how Digger spends
her days
Hard on the outside but
sweet deep inside
Basking in the sun and
riding the tide!

68

ty
OFFICIAL CLUB

4027
©1998 TY INC BEANIE BABIES OFFICIAL CLUB

LITTLE-KNOWN FACTS:
A crab is an invertebrate
called a crustacean –
which means it has many
jointed legs and an
external shell, called a
carapace. Most crabs
travel along the sand by
running sideways on the
very tips of their legs.

Moderate

Easy

Doby • 4110

DOBY
the Doberman

BEANIE BABIES

ty
OFFICIAL CLUB

Series I
4110
1998

Moderate

Easy

BEANIE BABIES OFFICIAL CLUB™

DOBY
the Doberman
Birthday: 10-9-96
Issued: 1-1-97

This dog is little but he
has might
Keep him close when you
sleep at night
He lays around with
nothing to do
Until he sees it's time to
protect you!

69

ty
OFFICIAL CLUB

4110
©1998 TY INC BEANIE BABIES OFFICIAL CLUB

LITTLE-KNOWN FACTS:
Doberman pinschers got
their name from Louis
Doberman, the German
who first raised them in
the 1890's. They are
very intelligent dogs, as
well as swift runners,
which is why they are
often used for police work.

Date Purchased: _____

Price Paid: _____

Market Value: _____

Purchased At: _____

COMMON CARDS

24

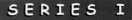

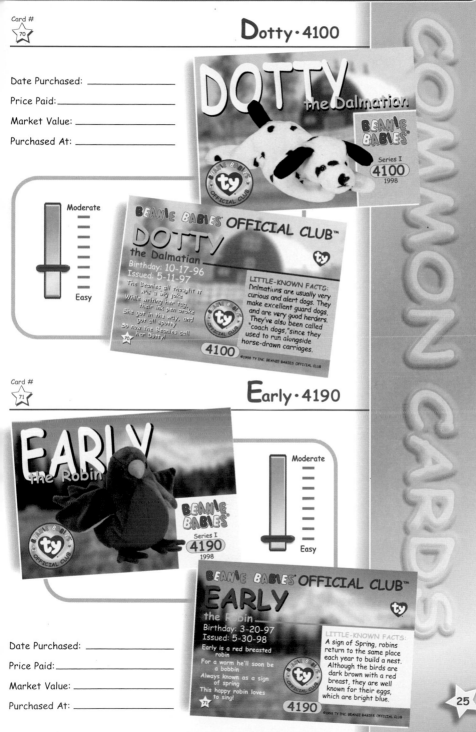

Card #
⭐ 70

Dotty • 4100

Date Purchased: _____

Price Paid: _____

Market Value: _____

Purchased At: _____

Moderate

Easy

DOTTY
the Dalmatian

BEANIE BABIES

Series I
4100
1998

BEANIE BABIES OFFICIAL CLUB™

DOTTY
the Dalmatian
Birthday: 10-17-96
Issued: 5-11-97

The Beanies all thought it
was a big joke
While writing her tag,
their ink pen broke
She got in the way, and
got all spotty
So now the Beanies call
her Dotty!

⭐ 70

LITTLE-KNOWN FACTS:
Dalmatians are usually very
curious and alert dogs. They
make excellent guard dogs,
and are very good herders.
They've also been called
"coach dogs," since they
used to run alongside
horse-drawn carriages.

4100
©1998 TY INC. BEANIE BABIES OFFICIAL CLUB

Card #
⭐ 71

Early • 4190

EARLY
the Robin

BEANIE BABIES

Series I
4190
1998

Moderate

Easy

BEANIE BABIES OFFICIAL CLUB™

EARLY
the Robin
Birthday: 3-20-97
Issued: 5-30-98

Early is a red breasted
robin
For a worm he'll soon be
a bobbin
Always known as a sign
of spring
This happy robin loves
to sing!

LITTLE-KNOWN FACTS:
A sign of Spring, robins
return to the same place
each year to build a nest.
Although the birds are
dark brown with a red
breast, they are well
known for their eggs,
which are bright blue.

4190
©1998 TY INC. BEANIE BABIES OFFICIAL CLUB

Date Purchased: _____

Price Paid: _____

Market Value: _____

Purchased At: _____

COMMON CARDS

25

1st Edition

COMMON CARDS

Ears · 4018

Card # 72

Date Purchased: _____

Price Paid: _____

Market Value: _____

Purchased At: _____

EARS the Rabbit

Series I
4018
1998

BEANIE BABIES OFFICIAL CLUB

EARS
the Rabbit
Birthday: 4-18-95
Issued: 1-7-96
He's been eating carrots so long
Didn't understand what was wrong
Couldn't see the board during classes
Until the doctor gave him glasses!

LITTLE-KNOWN FACTS:
Rabbits are one of the most prolific mammals found in North America. Most species raise anywhere from 2 to 5 litters per year, and each litter may contain 3 to 5 baby rabbits — that's a lot of bunnies!

72
4018
©1998 TY INC. BEANIE BABIES OFFICIAL CLUB

Moderate
Easy

Echo · 4180

Card # 73

Moderate
Easy

ECHO the Dolphin

Series I
4180
1998

BEANIE BABIES OFFICIAL CLUB

ECHO
the Dolphin
Birthday: 12-21-96
Issued: 5-11-97
Echo the dolphin lives in the sea
Playing with her friends, like you and me
Through the waves she echoes the sound
"I'm so glad to have you around!"

LITTLE-KNOWN FACTS:
Dolphins are the smallest member of the whale family. This Beanie Baby® was named after an "echo" - which is the repetition of a sound caused by the reflection of sound waves from a surface.

73
4180
©1998 TY INC. BEANIE BABIES OFFICIAL CLUB

Date Purchased: _____

Price Paid: _____

Market Value: _____

Purchased At: _____

SERIES I

Card #
74

Fleece • 4125

Date Purchased: _____

Price Paid: _____

Market Value: _____

Purchased At: _____

FLEECE
the Lamb

BEANIE BABIES
Series I
4125
1998

Moderate

Easy

BEANIE BABIES OFFICIAL CLUB™
FLEECE
the Lamb
Birthday: 3-21-96
Issued: 1-1-97
Fleece would like to
sing a lullaby
But please be patient,
she's rather shy
When you sleep, keep
her by your ear
Her song will leave you
nothing to fear.

ty

LITTLE-KNOWN FACTS:
Fleece is another name
for a sheep's fur. A sheep
is shorn and this fleece is
spun into wool — which is
used to make products
such as sweaters and rugs.

4125   ©1998 TY INC. BEANIE BABIES OFFICIAL CLUB

Card #
75

Flip • 4012

FLIP
the Cat

BEANIE BABIES
Series I
4012
1998

Moderate

Easy

BEANIE BABIES OFFICIAL CLUB™
FLIP
the Cat
Birthday: 2-28-95
Issued: 1-7-96
Flip the cat is an acrobat
She loves playing on
her mat
This cat flips with such
grace and flair
She can somersault in
mid air!

ty

LITTLE-KNOWN FACTS:
Cats are extremely curious
animals. Sometimes their
curiosity leads them to
unexpected places, and
heights! However, when
a cat falls, it usually
manages to gracefully land
on its feet.

4012   ©1998 TY INC. BEANIE BABIES OFFICIAL CLUB

Date Purchased: _____

Price Paid: _____

Market Value: _____

Purchased At: _____

COMMON CARDS

27

1st Edition

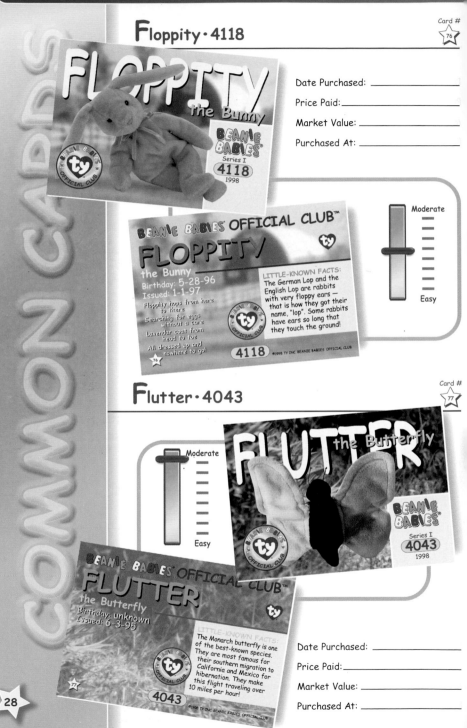

Floppity • 4118

Card #
76

FLOPPITY
the Bunny

BEANIE BABIES®
Series I
4118
1998

Date Purchased: _____

Price Paid: _____

Market Value: _____

Purchased At: _____

BEANIE BABIES® OFFICIAL CLUB™

FLOPPITY
the Bunny
Birthday: 5-28-96
Issued: 1-1-97
Floppity hops from here
to there
Searching for eggs
without a care
Lavendar coat from
head to toe
All dressed up and
nowhere to go!

LITTLE-KNOWN FACTS:
The German Lop and the
English Lop are rabbits
with very floppy ears —
that is how they got their
name, "lop". Some rabbits
have ears so long that
they touch the ground!

4118 ©1998 TY INC BEANIE BABIES OFFICIAL CLUB

Moderate

Easy

Flutter • 4043

Card #
77

Moderate

Easy

FLUTTER
the Butterfly

BEANIE
BABIES®
Series I
4043
1998

BEANIE BABIES® OFFICIAL CLUB™

FLUTTER
the Butterfly
Birthday: unknown
Issued: 6-3-95

LITTLE-KNOWN FACTS:
The Monarch butterfly is one
of the best-known species.
They are most famous for
their southern migration to
California and Mexico for
hibernation. They make
this flight traveling over
10 miles per hour!

4043 ©1998 TY INC BEANIE BABIES OFFICIAL CLUB

Date Purchased: _____

Price Paid: _____

Market Value: _____

Purchased At: _____

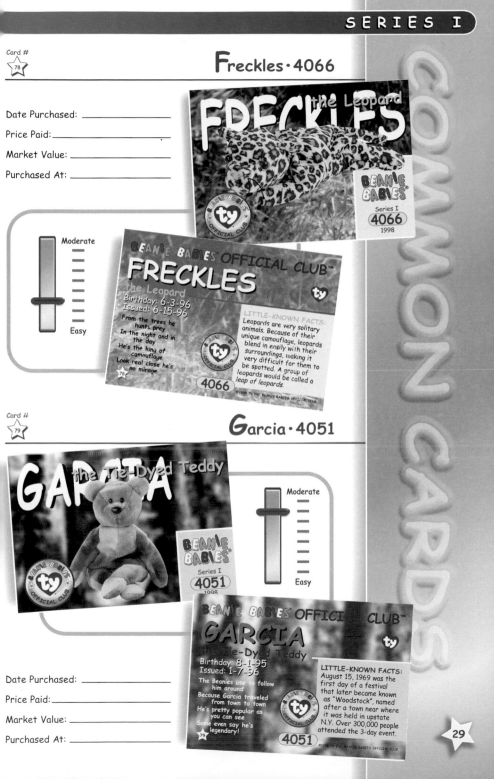

Card #
78

Freckles•4066

Date Purchased: _____

Price Paid: _____

Market Value: _____

Purchased At: _____

Moderate

Easy

FRECKLES the Leopard
Series I
4066
1998

BEANIE BABIES® OFFICIAL CLUB™
FRECKLES
the Leopard
Birthday: 6-3-96
Issued: 6-15-96
From the trees he
hunts prey
In the night and in
the day
He's the king of
camouflage
Look real close he's
no mirage.

LITTLE-KNOWN FACTS:
Leopards are very solitary
animals. Because of their
unique camouflage, leopards
blend in easily with their
surroundings, making it
very difficult for them to
be spotted. A group of
leopards would be called a
leap of leopards.

4066

Card #
79

Garcia•4051

GARCIA the Tie-Dyed Teddy
Series I
4051
1998

Moderate

Easy

BEANIE BABIES® OFFICIAL CLUB™
GARCIA
Tie-Dyed Teddy
Birthday: 8-1-95
Issued: 1-7-96
The Beanies use to follow
him around
Because Garcia traveled
from town to town
He's pretty popular as
you can see
Some even say he's
legendary!

LITTLE-KNOWN FACTS:
August 15, 1969 was the
first day of a festival
that later became known
as "Woodstock", named
after a town near where
it was held in upstate
N.Y. Over 300,000 people
attended the 3-day event.

4051

Date Purchased: _____

Price Paid: _____

Market Value: _____

Purchased At: _____

29

COMMON CARDS

1st Edition

COMMON CARDS

Gigi • 4191

Card # 80

Date Purchased: _____

Price Paid: _____

Market Value: _____

Purchased At: _____

BEANIE BABIES OFFICIAL CLUB™

GIGI
the Poodle

Birthday: 4-7-97
Issued: 5-30-98

Prancing and dancing
all down the street
Thinking her hairdo is
oh so neat
Always so careful in the
wind and rain
She's a dog that is
anything but plain!

80

4191

LITTLE-KNOWN FACTS:
Poodles are one of the
most popular breeds of
dogs in the United States.
They are also one of the
smartest. They are found
in three different sizes –
standard, miniature and
toy!

©1998 TY INC BEANIE BABIES OFFICIAL CLUB

Moderate

Easy

Gobbles • 4034

Card # 81

Moderate

Easy

BEANIE BABIES OFFICIAL CLUB™

GOBBLES
the Turkey

Birthday: 11-27-96
Issued: 10-1-97

Gobbles the turkey
loves to eat
Once a year she has
a feast
I have a secret I'd like
to divulge
If she eats too much her
tummy will bulge!

81

4034

LITTLE-KNOWN FACTS:
Male turkeys are called
toms, female turkeys are
called hens, and their young
are called poults. Most
turkeys, like Gobbles, tend
to roost in trees rather
than sleep on the ground!

©1998 TY INC BEANIE BABIES OFFICIAL CLUB

Date Purchased: _____

Price Paid: _____

Market Value: _____

Purchased At: _____

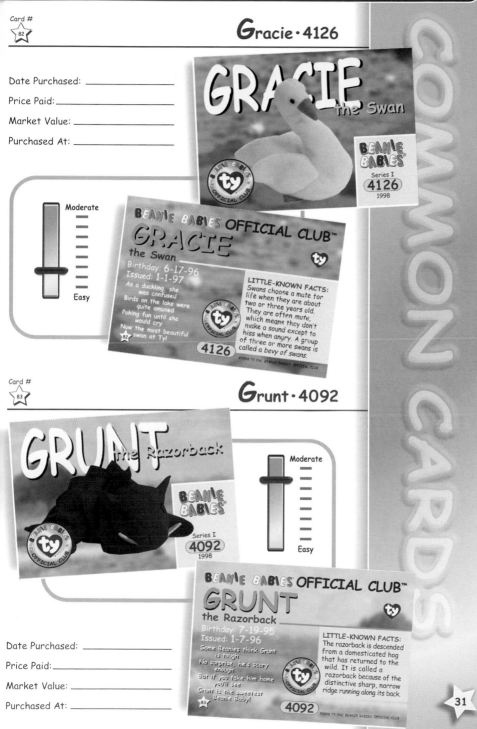

Card #
82

*G*racie • 4126

Date Purchased: _____

Price Paid: _____

Market Value: _____

Purchased At: _____

Moderate

Easy

BEANIE BABIES OFFICIAL CLUB™
GRACIE
the Swan
Birthday: 6-17-96
Issued: 1-1-97
As a duckling, she
was confused
Birds on the lake were
quite amused
Poking fun until she
would cry
Now the most beautiful
swan at Ty!

LITTLE-KNOWN FACTS:
Swans choose a mate for
life when they are about
two or three years old.
They are often mute,
which means they don't
make a sound except to
hiss when angry. A group
of three or more swans is
called a bevy of swans.
©1998 TY INC. BEANIE BABIES OFFICIAL CLUB

4126

GRACIE
the Swan

BEANIE BABIES
Series I
4126
1998

Card #
83

*G*runt • 4092

GRUNT
the Razorback

BEANIE BABIES
Series I
4092
1998

Moderate

Easy

BEANIE BABIES OFFICIAL CLUB™
GRUNT
the Razorback
Birthday: 7-19-95
Issued: 1-7-96
Some Beanies think Grunt
is tough
No surprise, he's scary
enough
But if you take him home
you'll see
Grunt is the sweetest
Beanie Baby!

LITTLE-KNOWN FACTS:
The razorback is descended
from a domesticated hog
that has returned to the
wild. It is called a
razorback because of the
distinctive sharp, narrow
ridge running along its back.

4092

Date Purchased: _____

Price Paid: _____

Market Value: _____

Purchased At: _____

COMMON CARDS

31

COMMON CARDS

Happy • 4061

Card #
84

HAPPY
the Gray Hippo

BEANIE BABIES

Series I
4061
1998

Date Purchased: _____

Price Paid: _____

Market Value: _____

Purchased At: _____

BEANIE BABIES OFFICIAL CLUB™

HAPPY
the Gray Hippo
Birthday: 2-25-94
Issued: 6-25-94
Happy the Hippo loves
to wade
In the river and in
the shade
When Happy shoots water
out of his snout
You know he's happy
without a doubt!

84

ty

LITTLE-KNOWN FACTS:
The hippopotamus is native
to Africa. It spends up to
18 hours a day in the water
to help keep cool. A hippo
can stay submerged for
as long as 5 minutes as it
walks along the bottom
of rivers and lakes.

4061
©1998 TY INC. BEANIE BABIES OFFICIAL CLUB.

Moderate

Easy

Hissy • 4185

Card #
85

Moderate

Easy

HISSY
the Snake

BEANIE BABIES

Series I
4185
1998

BEANIE BABIES OFFICIAL CLUB™

HISSY
the Snake
Birthday: 4-4-97
Issued: 12-31-97
Curled and coiled and ready
to play
He waits for you patiently
every day
He'll keep his best friend
but not his skin
And stay with you through
thick and thin!

85

ty

LITTLE-KNOWN FACTS:
The python uses its darting
tongue to detect the scent
of other animals close by.
Pythons are great swimmers
and can stay under water
for as long as 30 minutes
without coming up for air.

4185
©1998 TY INC. BEANIE BABIES OFFICIAL CLUB.

Date Purchased: _____

Price Paid: _____

Market Value: _____

Purchased At: _____

COMMON CARDS

Card #
86

Hoot • 4073

Date Purchased: _____

Price Paid: _____

Market Value: _____

Purchased At: _____

Moderate

Easy

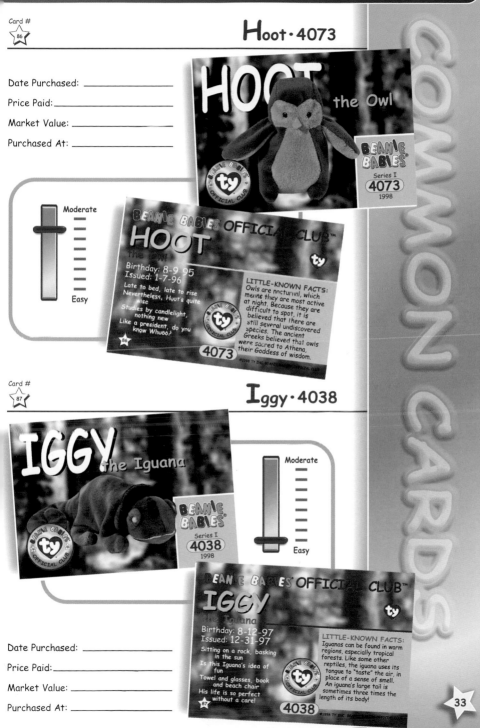

HOOT the Owl

BEANIE BABIES®
Series I
4073
1998

BEANIE BABIES OFFICIAL CLUB™

HOOT
the Owl

Birthday: 8-9-95
Issued: 1-7-96

Late to bed, late to rise
Nevertheless, Hoot's quite wise
Studies by candlelight,
nothing new
Like a president, do you
know Whooo?

LITTLE-KNOWN FACTS:
Owls are nocturnal, which
means they are most active
at night. Because they are
difficult to spot, it is
believed that there are
still several undiscovered
species. The ancient
Greeks believed that owls
were sacred to Athena,
their Goddess of wisdom.

4073

©1998 TY INC. BEANIE BABIES OFFICIAL CLUB

Card #
87

Iggy • 4038

IGGY the Iguana

BEANIE BABIES®
Series I
4038
1998

Moderate

Easy

BEANIE BABIES OFFICIAL CLUB™

IGGY
the Iguana

Birthday: 8-12-97
Issued: 12-31-97

Sitting on a rock, basking
in the sun
Is this Iguana's idea of
fun
Towel and glasses, book
and beach chair
His life is so perfect
without a care!

LITTLE-KNOWN FACTS:
Iguanas can be found in warm
regions, especially tropical
forests. Like some other
reptiles, the iguana uses its
tongue to "taste" the air, in
place of a sense of smell.
An iguana's large tail is
sometimes three times the
length of its body!

4038

©1998 TY INC. BEANIE BABIES OFFICIAL CLUB

Date Purchased: _____

Price Paid: _____

Market Value: _____

Purchased At: _____

33

Inch · 4044

Card #
88

INCH the Inchworm

BEANIE BABIES
OFFICIAL CLUB
Series I
4044
1998

Date Purchased: _____

Price Paid: _____

Market Value: _____

Purchased At: _____

BEANIE BABIES OFFICIAL CLUB
INCH the Inchworm
Birthday: 9-3-95
Issued: 6-3-95
Inch the worm is a friend of mine
He goes so slow all the time
Inching around from here to there
Traveling the world without a care!
88
4044

LITTLE-KNOWN FACTS:
Inchworms are named for the way they "inch" along by extending their front legs forward, then pulling their back legs up to meet them. Inchworms build a cocoon of silk in which they transform into a moth.
©1998 TY INC. BEANIE BABIES OFFICIAL CLUB

Moderate
Easy

Inky · 4028

Card #
89

Moderate
Easy

INKY the Pink Octopus

BEANIE BABIES
OFFICIAL CLUB
Series I
4028
1998

BEANIE BABIES OFFICIAL CLUB
INKY the Pink Octopus
Birthday: 11-29-94
Issued: 6-3-95
Inky's head is big and round
As he swims he makes no sound
If you need a hand, don't hesitate
Inky can help because he has eight!
89
4028

LITTLE-KNOWN FACTS:
The octopus belongs to a family of animals known as mollusks – which are sea animals with no bones. Octopuses make their homes in a hole or rock crevice – and they can change color to blend in with their surroundings!
©1998 TY INC. BEANIE BABIES OFFICIAL CLUB

Date Purchased: _____

Price Paid: _____

Market Value: _____

Purchased At: _____

COMMON CARDS

COMMON CARDS

Card #
90

Jabber • 4197

Date Purchased: _____

Price Paid: _____

Market Value: _____

Purchased At: _____

Moderate — Easy

JABBER
the Parrot

BEANIE BABIES
Series I
4197
1998

BEANIE BABIES OFFICIAL CLUB™
JABBER
the Parrot
Birthday: 10-10-97
Issued: 5-30-98
Teaching Jabber to move his beak
A large vocabulary he now can speak
Jabber will repeat what you say
Teach him a new word everyday!
90
LITTLE-KNOWN FACTS:
Parrots are a large family of brightly-colored tropical birds. There are over 300 different species. Some species make good pets because they are sociable and like to chatter!
4197
©1998 TY INC. BEANIE BABIES OFFICIAL CLUB

Card #
91

Jake • 4199

JAKE
the Mallard Duck

BEANIE BABIES
Series I
4199
1998

Moderate — Easy

BEANIE BABIES OFFICIAL CLUB™
JAKE
the Mallard Duck
Birthday: 4-16-97
Issued: 5-30-98
Jake the drake likes to splash in a puddle
Take him home and give him a cuddle
Quack, Quack, Quack, he will say
He's so glad you're here to play!
91
LITTLE-KNOWN FACTS:
The Mallard is the largest of all ducks. In the spring, the male has a distinctive green head with a white ring around his neck. In the winter he molts, trading his bright plumage for brown, more closely resembling the female.
4199
©1998 TY INC. BEANIE BABIES OFFICIAL CLUB

Date Purchased: _____

Price Paid: _____

Market Value: _____

Purchased At: _____

35

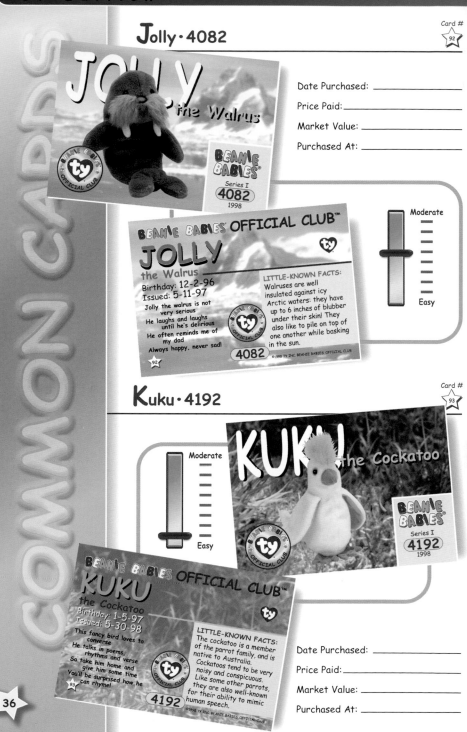

Jolly · 4082

Card #
92

Date Purchased: _____

Price Paid: _____

Market Value: _____

Purchased At: _____

JOLLY
the Walrus

Series I
4082
1998

BEANIE BABIES OFFICIAL CLUB™

JOLLY
the Walrus

Birthday: 12-2-96
Issued: 5-11-97

Jolly the walrus is not
very serious
He laughs and laughs
until he's delirious
He often reminds me of
my dad
Always happy, never sad!

LITTLE-KNOWN FACTS:
Walruses are well
insulated against icy
Arctic waters; they have
up to 6 inches of blubber
under their skin! They
also like to pile on top of
one another while basking
in the sun.

92

4082

©1998 TY INC. BEANIE BABIES OFFICIAL CLUB

Moderate

Easy

Kuku · 4192

Card #
93

Moderate

Easy

KUKU
the Cockatoo

Series I
4192
1998

BEANIE BABIES OFFICIAL CLUB™

KUKU
the Cockatoo

Birthday: 1-5-97
Issued: 5-30-98

This fancy bird loves to
converse
He talks in poems,
rhythms and verse
So take him home and
give him some time
You'll be surprised how he
can rhyme!

LITTLE-KNOWN FACTS:
The cockatoo is a member
of the parrot family, and is
native to Australia.
Cockatoos tend to be very
noisy and conspicuous.
Like some other parrots,
they are also well-known
for their ability to mimic
human speech.

93

4192

©1998 TY INC. BEANIE BABIES OFFICIAL CLUB

Date Purchased: _____

Price Paid: _____

Market Value: _____

Purchased At: _____

COMMON CARDS

COMMON CARDS

Card #
94

Libearty • 4057

Date Purchased: _____

Price Paid: _____

Market Value: _____

Purchased At: _____

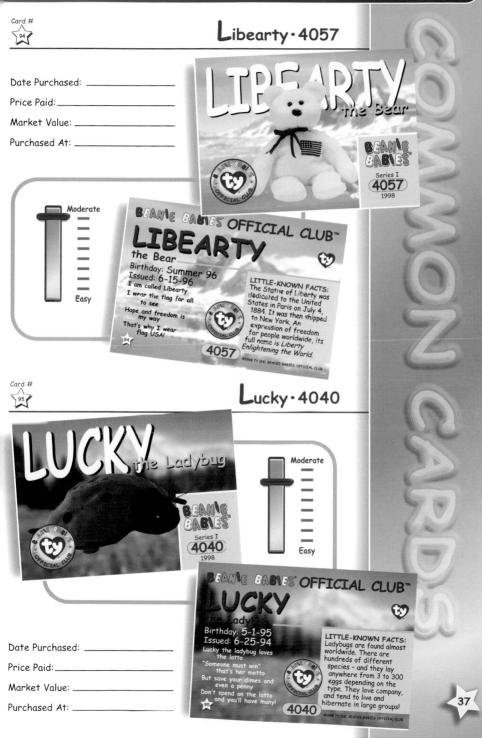

Moderate

Easy

Card #
95

Lucky • 4040

Moderate

Easy

Date Purchased: _____

Price Paid: _____

Market Value: _____

Purchased At: _____

37

1st Edition

COMMON CARDS

Magic · 4088

Card #
96

Date Purchased: _____

Price Paid: _____

Market Value: _____

Purchased At: _____

BEANIE BABIES OFFICIAL CLUB™

MAGIC
the Dragon
Birthday: 9-5-95
Issued: 6-3-95
Magic the dragon lives in
a dream
The most beautiful that
you have ever seen
Through magic lands she
likes to fly
Look up and watch her,
way up high!
96

4088

LITTLE-KNOWN FACTS:
According to the Chinese
Zodiac, 1999 is the Year
of the Dragon. January
6, 1999, marks the
beginning of the Chinese
New Year.

Moderate

Easy

Manny · 4081

Card #
97

Moderate

Easy

MANNY
the Manatee

BEANIE BABIES
Series I
4081
1998

BEANIE BABIES OFFICIAL CLUB™

MANNY
the Manatee
Birthday: 6-8-95
Issued: 1-7-96
Manny is sometimes called
a sea cow
She likes to twirl and
likes to bow
Manny sure is glad you
bought her
Because it's so lonely
under water
97

4081

LITTLE-KNOWN FACTS:
Manatees are sometimes
called Sea Cows because
they resemble cows
grazing when they eat
sea plants. A full-grown
manatee can weigh up to
3500 lbs. and eats 100 lbs.
of sea plants each day!

Date Purchased: _____

Price Paid: _____

Market Value: _____

Purchased At: _____

COMMON CARDS

Card #
98

Mystic · 4007

Date Purchased: _____

Price Paid: _____

Market Value: _____

Purchased At: _____

Moderate

Easy

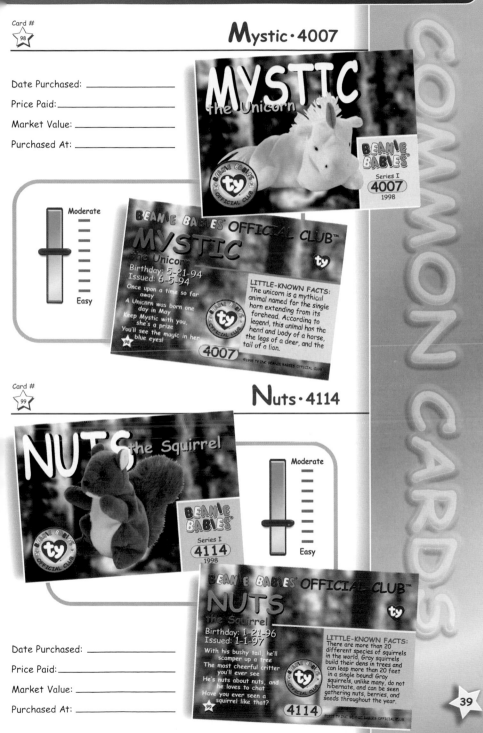

Card #
99

Nuts · 4114

Moderate

Easy

Date Purchased: _____

Price Paid: _____

Market Value: _____

Purchased At: _____

39

1st Edition

Peace • 4053

Card # 100

Date Purchased: _____

Price Paid: _____

Market Value: _____

Purchased At: _____

Moderate — Easy

PEACE the Tie-Dyed Bear
Birthday: 2-1-96
Issued: 5-11-97

All races, all colors,
under the sun
Join hands together and
have some fun
Dance to the music, rock
and roll is the sound
Symbols of peace and
love abound!

LITTLE-KNOWN FACTS:
The Nobel Prizes are the international awards given annually, honoring outstanding achievement in 6 different fields of study. The Peace Prize is given in the interest of promoting world peace.

4053

©1998 TY INC. BEANIE BABIES OFFICIAL CLUB

Peanut • 4062

Card # 101

Moderate — Easy

PEANUT the Light Blue Elephant
Birthday: 1-25-95
Issued: 10-2-95

Peanut the elephant walks
on tip-toes
Quietly sneaking wherever
she goes
She'll sneak up on you and
a hug you will get
Peanut is a friend you
won't soon forget!

LITTLE-KNOWN FACTS:
The first elephant to come to the U.S. arrived in New York from India in 1796. Elephants living in the wild can walk very quickly — when a herd is on the move, it can cover as much as 50 miles a day.

4062

©1998 TY INC. BEANIE BABIES OFFICIAL CLUB

Date Purchased: _____

Price Paid: _____

Market Value: _____

Purchased At: _____

COMMON CARDS

Card #
102

Pouch • 4161

Date Purchased: _____

Price Paid: _____

Market Value: _____

Purchased At: _____

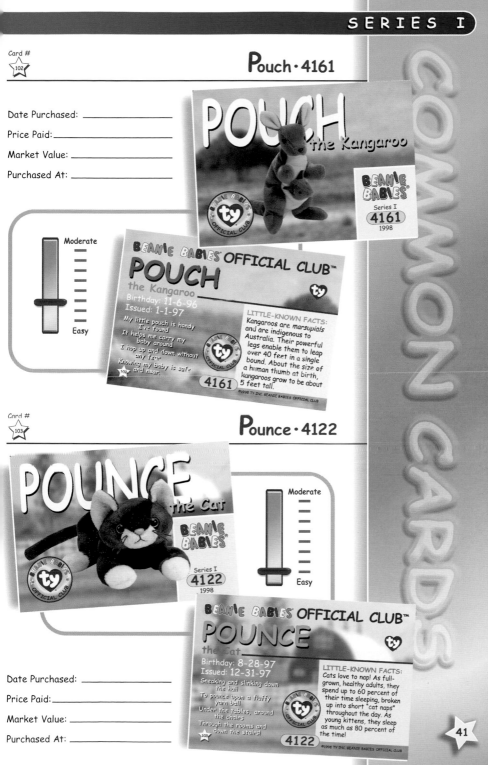

POUCH
the Kangaroo

BEANIE BABIES
Series I
4161
1998

Moderate

Easy

BEANIE BABIES OFFICIAL CLUB™
POUCH
the Kangaroo
Birthday: 11-6-96
Issued: 1-1-97

My little pouch is handy
I've found
It helps me carry my
baby around
I hop up and down without
any fear
Knowing my baby is safe
and near.

LITTLE-KNOWN FACTS:
Kangaroos are *marsupials*
and are indigenous to
Australia. Their powerful
legs enable them to leap
over 40 feet in a single
bound. About the size of
a human thumb at birth,
kangaroos grow to be about
5 feet tall.

4161

©1998 TY INC. BEANIE BABIES OFFICIAL CLUB

Card #
103

Pounce • 4122

POUNCE
the Cat

BEANIE BABIES

Series I
4122
1998

Moderate

Easy

BEANIE BABIES OFFICIAL CLUB™
POUNCE
the Cat
Birthday: 8-28-97
Issued: 12-31-97

Sneaking and slinking down
the hall
To pounce upon a fluffy
yarn ball
Under the tables, around
the chairs
Through the rooms and
down the stairs!

LITTLE-KNOWN FACTS:
Cats love to nap! As full-
grown, healthy adults, they
spend up to 60 percent of
their time sleeping, broken
up into short "cat naps"
throughout the day. As
young kittens, they sleep
as much as 80 percent of
the time!

4122

©1998 TY INC. BEANIE BABIES OFFICIAL CLUB

Date Purchased: _____

Price Paid: _____

Market Value: _____

Purchased At: _____

41

COMMON CARDS

COMMON CARDS

Prance • 4123

PRANCE the Cat

BEANIE BABIES
Series I
4123
1998

BEANIE BABIES OFFICIAL CLUB
PRANCE
the Cat
Birthday: 11-20-97
Issued: 12-31-97

She darts around and
swats the air
Then looks confused when
nothing's there
Pick her up and pet her
soft fur
Listen closely, and you'll
hear her purr!

LITTLE-KNOWN FACTS:
All cats have whiskers on
their faces - on either side
of the mouth, and even
above their eyes. Cats'
whiskers are very
sensitive and help them
sense their surroundings.
In dark places, a cat's
whiskers act as its sight!

104
4123
©1998 TY INC BEANIE BABIES OFFICIAL CLUB

Moderate
Easy

Date Purchased: _____
Price Paid: _____
Market Value: _____
Purchased At: _____

Puffer • 4181

Moderate
Easy

PUFFER the Puffin

BEANIE BABIES
Series I
4181
1998

BEANIE BABIES OFFICIAL CLUB
PUFFER
the Puffin
Birthday: 11-3-97
Issued: 12-31-97

What in the world does a
puffin do?
We're sure that you would
like to know too
We asked Puffer how she
spends her days
Before she answered, she
flew away!

LITTLE-KNOWN FACTS:
The puffin is a small sea
bird that lives in the chilly
waters of the Arctic
circle. Its bright,
colorful beak, which
helps attract a mate,
fades to gray when
breeding season ends.

105
4181
©1998 TY INC BEANIE BABIES OFFICIAL CLUB

Date Purchased: _____
Price Paid: _____
Market Value: _____
Purchased At: _____

Card #
106

Pugsly • 4106

Date Purchased: _____

Price Paid: _____

Market Value: _____

Purchased At: _____

Moderate

Easy

BEANIE BABIES® OFFICIAL CLUB™
PUGSLY
the Pug Dog
Birthday: 5-2-96
Issued: 5-11-97
Pugsly is picky about what
he will wear
Never a spot, a stain
or a tear
Image is something of
which he'll gloat
Until he noticed his
wrinkled coat!

LITTLE-KNOWN FACTS:
Pug dogs were originally
raised in China in the 1700s.
Although they usually weigh
less than 18 lbs, pug dogs
are the largest of the toy
dog breeds.

4106

©1998 TY INC. BEANIE BABIES OFFICIAL CLUB

Card #
107

Rainbow • 4037

BEANIE BABIES® OFFICIAL CLUB™
RAINBOW
the Chameleon
Birthday: 10-14-97
Issued: 12-31-97
Red, green, blue and
yellow
This chameleon is a
colorful fellow
A blend of colors, his
own unique hue
Rainbow was made
especially for you!

LITTLE-KNOWN FACTS:
The chameleon is a reptile
which commonly lives in trees
in northern African and southern Mediterranean regions.
They are best known for their
ability to change color rapidly,
allowing them to blend in with
their environment. Another
unique feature is that
chameleons can move both eyes
together, or one at a time!

4037

©1998 TY INC. BEANIE BABIES OFFICIAL CLUB

Date Purchased: _____

Price Paid: _____

Market Value: _____

Purchased At: _____

43

1st Edition

COMMON CARDS

Rex·4086

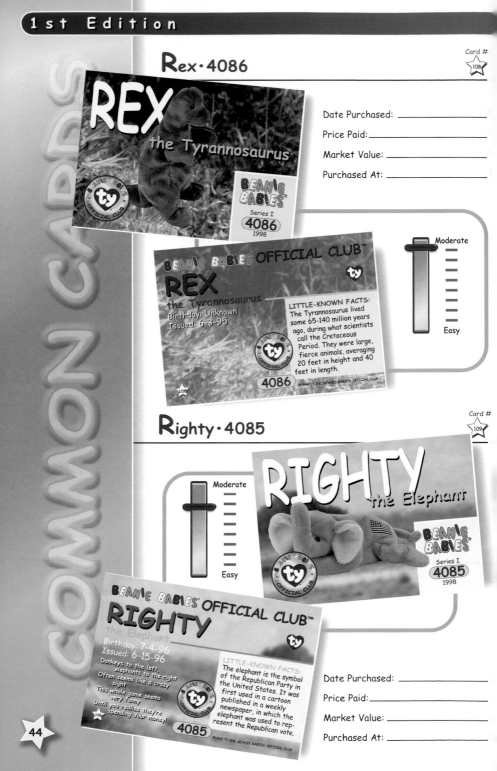

REX
the Tyrannosaurus

Series I
4086
1998

BEANIE BABIES OFFICIAL CLUB™
REX
the Tyrannosaurus
Birthday: Unknown
Issued: 6-3-95

LITTLE-KNOWN FACTS:
The Tyrannosaurus lived some 65-140 million years ago, during what scientists call the Cretaceous Period. They were large, fierce animals, averaging 20 feet in height and 40 feet in length.

4086

Moderate — Easy

Date Purchased: _____
Price Paid: _____
Market Value: _____
Purchased At: _____

Righty·4085

RIGHTY
the Elephant

Series I
4085
1998

Moderate — Easy

BEANIE BABIES OFFICIAL CLUB™
RIGHTY
the Elephant
Birthday: 7-4-96
Issued: 6-15-96

Donkeys to the left,
elephants to the right
Often seems like a crazy sight
This whole game seems very funny
Until you realize they're spending your money!

LITTLE-KNOWN FACTS:
The elephant is the symbol of the Republican Party in the United States. It was first used in a cartoon published in a weekly newspaper, in which the elephant was used to represent the Republican vote.

4085

Date Purchased: _____
Price Paid: _____
Market Value: _____
Purchased At: _____

COMMON CARDS

Card #
110

Ringo • 4014

Date Purchased: _____

Price Paid: _____

Market Value: _____

Purchased At: _____

Moderate

Easy

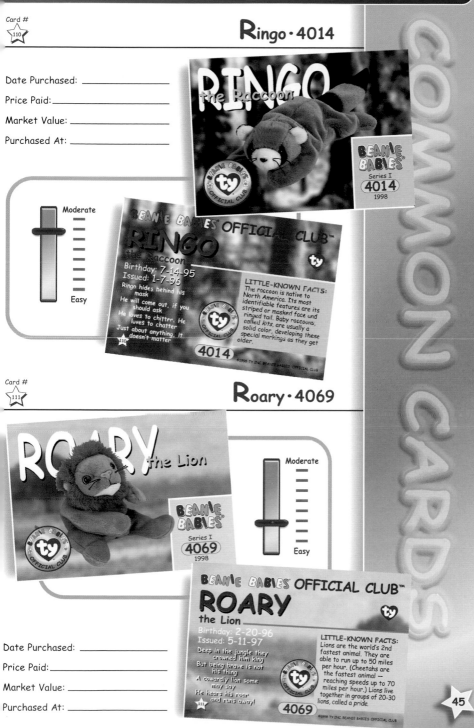

Card #
111

Roary • 4069

Moderate

Easy

Date Purchased: _____

Price Paid: _____

Market Value: _____

Purchased At: _____

45

1st Edition

COMMON CARDS

Rocket • 4202

Card #
112

ROCKET
the Bluejay

BEANIE BABIES OFFICIAL CLUB
Series I
4202
1998

BEANIE BABIES OFFICIAL CLUB™
ROCKET
the Bluejay
Birthday: 3-12-97
Issued: 5-30-98
Rocket is the fastest
blue jay ever
He flies in all sorts
of weather
Aerial tricks are his
specialty
He's so entertaining for
you and me!
112
4202

LITTLE-KNOWN FACTS:
The blue jay is related to
the crow, and is commonly
found in eastern United
States, as well as in
Canada. It is easily
identified by its gray-blue
and bright blue plumage,
as well as the blue crest
on its head!

©1998 TY INC. BEANIE BABIES OFFICIAL CLUB

Moderate

Easy

Date Purchased: _____
Price Paid: _____
Market Value: _____
Purchased At: _____

Rover • 4101

Card #
113

Moderate

Easy

ROVER
the Dog

BEANIE BABIES
Series I
4101
1998

BEANIE BABIES OFFICIAL CLUB™
ROVER
the Dog
Birthday: 5-30-96
Issued: 6-15-96
This dog is red and his
name is Rover
If you call him he is sure
to come over
He barks and plays with
all his might
But worry not, he won't
bite!
113
4101

LITTLE-KNOWN FACTS:
Many dogs turn around in
circles a few times before
lying down. This instinctive
behavior is inherited from
its wild ancestors who
may have had to trample
the dirt or grass to make
a bed.

©1998 TY INC. BEANIE BABIES OFFICIAL CLUB

Date Purchased: _____
Price Paid: _____
Market Value: _____
Purchased At: _____

COMMON CARDS

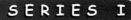

Card #
114

Scottie • 4102

Date Purchased: _____

Price Paid: _____

Market Value: _____

Purchased At: _____

SCOTTIE
the Scottish Terrier

BEANIE BABIES
Series I
4102
1998

Moderate

Easy

BEANIE BABIES OFFICIAL CLUB™
SCOTTIE
the Scottish Terrier
Birthday: 6-15-96
Issued: 6-15-96
Scottie is a friendly sort
Even though his legs are
short
He is always happy as
can be
His best friends are you
and me!

LITTLE-KNOWN FACTS:
Scottish terriers were
orginally raised in Scotland in
the 1800's. Their nickname
is "Scottie" which is how
this little Beanie™ got its
name. This brave dog only
weighs about 20 lbs. when
full-grown.

114

4102

©1998 TY INC. BEANIE BABIES OFFICIAL CLUB

Card #
115

Seamore • 4029

SEAMORE
the seal

BEANIE BABIES
Series I
4029
1998

Moderate

Easy

BEANIE BABIES OFFICIAL CLUB™
SEAMORE
the Seal
Birthday: 12-14-96
Issued: 6-25-94
Seamore is a little
white seal
Fish and clams are her
favorite meal
Playing and laughing in
the sand
She's the happiest seal in
the land!

LITTLE-KNOWN FACTS:
A group of seals is called
a pod of seals. Male seals
are called bulls, female
seals are called cows and
baby seals are called
pups.

4029

©1998 TY INC. BEANIE BABIES OFFICIAL CLUB

Date Purchased: _____

Price Paid: _____

Market Value: _____

Purchased At: _____

1st Edition

Seaweed · 4080

Card #
116

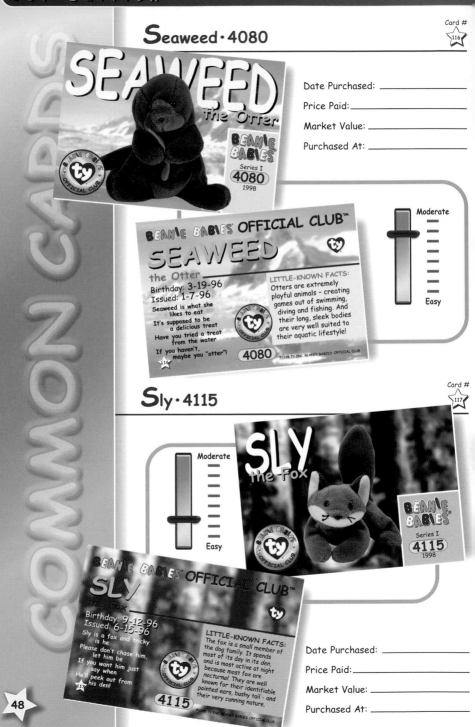

SEAWEED
the Otter

BEANIE BABIES
Series I
4080
1998

Date Purchased: _____

Price Paid: _____

Market Value: _____

Purchased At: _____

Moderate

Easy

BEANIE BABIES® OFFICIAL CLUB™
SEAWEED
the Otter
Birthday: 3-19-96
Issued: 1-7-96
Seaweed is what she
likes to eat
It's supposed to be
a delicious treat
Have you tried a treat
from the water
If you haven't,
maybe you "otter"!

LITTLE-KNOWN FACTS:
Otters are extremely
playful animals – creating
games out of swimming,
diving and fishing. And
their long, sleek bodies
are very well suited to
their aquatic lifestyle!

4080   ©1998 TY INC. BEANIE BABIES OFFICIAL CLUB

Sly · 4115

Card #
117

Moderate

Easy

SLY
the Fox

BEANIE BABIES
Series I
4115
1998

BEANIE BABIES® OFFICIAL CLUB™
SLY
the Fox
Birthday: 9-12-96
Issued: 6-15-96
Sly is a fox and tricky
is he
Please don't chase him,
let him be
If you want him just
say when
He'll peek out from
his den!

LITTLE-KNOWN FACTS:
The fox is a small member of
the dog family. It spends
most of its day in its den
and is most active at night
because most fox are
nocturnal. They are well
known for their identifiable
pointed ears, bushy tail – and
their very cunning nature.

4115   ©1998 TY INC. BEANIE BABIES OFFICIAL CLUB

Date Purchased: _____

Price Paid: _____

Market Value: _____

Purchased At: _____

Card # 118

Smoochy • 4039

Date Purchased: _____

Price Paid: _____

Market Value: _____

Purchased At: _____

SMOOCHY the Frog

BEANIE BABIES
Series I
4039
1998

Moderate

Easy

BEANIE BABIES OFFICIAL CLUB™
SMOOCHY
the Frog
Birthday: 10-1-97
Issued: 12-31-97
Is he a frog or maybe
a prince?
This confusion makes
him wince
Find the answer, help
him with this
Be the one to give
him a kiss!

LITTLE-KNOWN FACTS:
Frogs are *amphibians* which
means they are capable of
living both on land and in
the water. People often
confuse frugs and toads.
Frogs have smooth, wet
skin, while toads are
rough and dry.

4039
©1998 TY INC. BEANIE BABIES OFFICIAL CLUB

Card # 119

Snip • 4120

SNIP the Siamese Cat

BEANIE BABIES
Series I
4120
1998

Moderate

Easy

BEANIE BABIES OFFICIAL CLUB™
SNIP
the Siamese Cat
Birthday: 10-22-96
Issued: 1-1-97
Snip the cat is Siamese
She'll be your friend if
you please
So toss her a toy or a
piece of string
Playing with you is her
favorite thing!

LITTLE-KNOWN FACTS:
Siamese cats are slim, deli-
cate, short-haired cats,
originally raised by royalty
in Siam, now called Thailand.
These beautiful cats
became such cherished
companions that for many
years only royalty was
allowed to keep them as pets.

4120
©1998 TY INC. BEANIE BABIES OFFICIAL CLUB

Date Purchased: _____

Price Paid: _____

Market Value: _____

Purchased At: _____

49

COMMON CARDS

Snort • 4002

Card # 120

SNORT the Bull

BEANIE BABIES OFFICIAL CLUB

Series I
4002
1998

Date Purchased: _____

Price Paid: _____

Market Value: _____

Purchased At: _____

BEANIE BABIES OFFICIAL CLUB™

SNORT
the Bull

Birthday: 5-15-95
Issued: 1-1-97

Although Snort is not
so tall
He loves to play
basketball
He is a star player
in his dream
Can you guess his
favorite team?

LITTLE-KNOWN FACTS:
Cattle are very important
farm animals in the United
States. The female is called
a cow and the male is
called a bull. Bulls grow
to stand about 5 feet
tall, and can weigh over
2,000 lbs.

4002
©1998 TY INC. BEANIE BABIES OFFICIAL CLUB

Moderate

Easy

Snowball • 4201

Card # 121

Moderate

Easy

SNOWBALL the snowman

BEANIE BABIES

Series I
4201
1998

BEANIE BABIES OFFICIAL CLUB™

SNOWBALL
the Snowman

Birthday: 12-22-96
Issued: 10-1-97

There is a snowman, I've
been told
That plays with Beanies
out in the cold
What is better in a
winter wonderland
Than a Beanie snowman in
your hand?

LITTLE-KNOWN FACTS:
Snow is a formation of
tiny ice crystals. Each
snowflake is six-sided but
every one is different! In
1921, 76 inches of snow
fell in Silver Lake,
Colorado, during a 24-
hour period.

4201
©1998 TY INC. BEANIE BABIES OFFICIAL CLUB

Date Purchased: _____

Price Paid: _____

Market Value: _____

Purchased At: _____

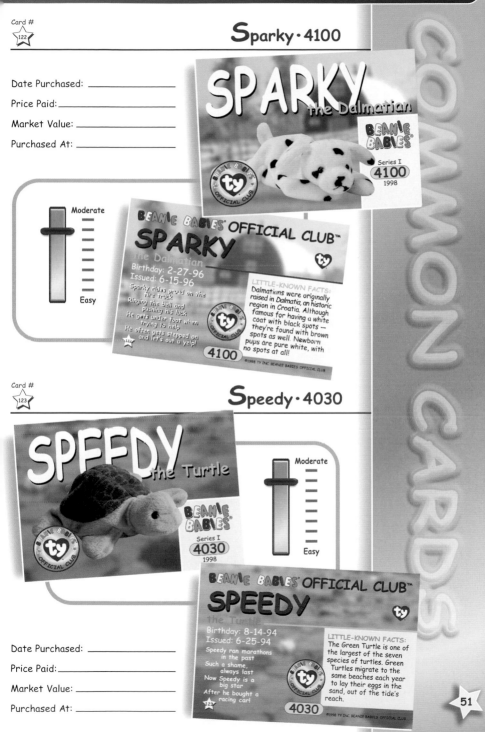

COMMON CARDS

Card
122

Sparky • 4100

Date Purchased: _____

Price Paid: _____

Market Value: _____

Purchased At: _____

Moderate

Easy

SPARKY
the Dalmatian

BEANIE BABIES

Series I
4100
1998

BEANIE BABIES OFFICIAL CLUB
SPARKY
the Dalmatian
Birthday: 2-27-96
Issued: 6-15-96
Sparky rides proud on the
fire truck
Ringing the bell and
pushing his luck
He gets under foot when
trying to help
He often gets stepped on
and let's out a yelp!

LITTLE-KNOWN FACTS!
Dalmatians were originally
raised in Dalmatia, an historic
region in Croatia. Although
famous for having a white
coat with black spots —
they're found with brown
spots as well. Newborn
pups are pure white, with
no spots at all!

4100
©1998 TY INC. BEANIE BABIES OFFICIAL CLUB

Card
123

Speedy • 4030

SPEEDY
the Turtle

BEANIE BABIES

Series I
4030
1998

Moderate

Easy

BEANIE BABIES OFFICIAL CLUB
SPEEDY
the Turtle
Birthday: 8-14-94
Issued: 6-25-94
Speedy ran marathons
in the past
Such a shame,
always last
Now Speedy is a
big star
After he bought a
racing car!

LITTLE-KNOWN FACTS:
The Green Turtle is one of
the largest of the seven
species of turtles. Green
Turtles migrate to the
same beaches each year
to lay their eggs in the
sand, out of the tide's
reach.

4030
©1998 TY INC. BEANIE BABIES OFFICIAL CLUB

Date Purchased: _____

Price Paid: _____

Market Value: _____

Purchased At: _____

1st Edition

COMMON CARDS

Spike · 4060

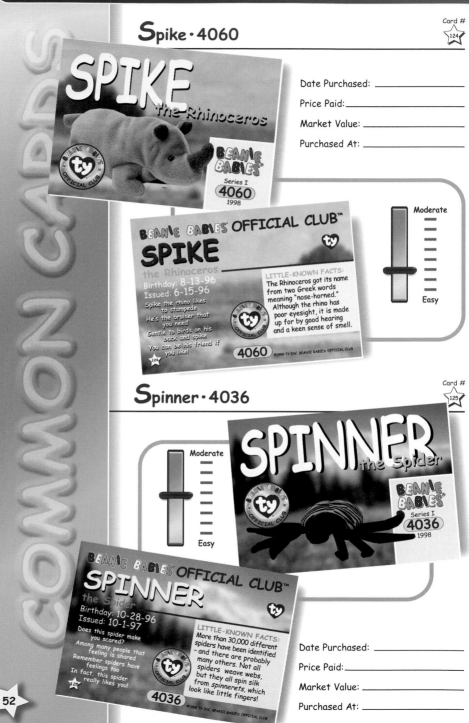

Date Purchased: _____

Price Paid: _____

Market Value: _____

Purchased At: _____

SPIKE the Rhinoceros
Series I
4060
1998

BEANIE BABIES OFFICIAL CLUB
SPIKE
the Rhinoceros
Birthday: 8-13-96
Issued: 6-15-96
Spike the rhino likes
to stampede
He's the bruiser that
you need
Gentle to birds on his
back and spike
You can be his friend if
you like!

LITTLE-KNOWN FACTS:
The Rhinoceros got its name
from two Greek words
meaning "nose-horned."
Although the rhino has
poor eyesight, it is made
up for by good hearing
and a keen sense of smell.

4060 ©1998 TY INC. BEANIE BABIES OFFICIAL CLUB

Moderate / Easy

Spinner · 4036

Moderate / Easy

SPINNER the Spider
Series I
4036
1998

BEANIE BABIES OFFICIAL CLUB
SPINNER
the Spider
Birthday: 10-28-96
Issued: 10-1-97
Does this spider make
you scared?
Among many people that
feeling is shared
Remember spiders have
feelings too
In fact, this spider
really likes you!

LITTLE-KNOWN FACTS:
More than 30,000 different
spiders have been identified
– and there are probably
many others. Not all
spiders weave webs,
but they all spin silk
from spinnerets, which
look like little fingers!

4036 ©1998 TY INC. BEANIE BABIES OFFICIAL CLUB

Date Purchased: _____

Price Paid: _____

Market Value: _____

Purchased At: _____

Card #
126

Spooky • 4090

Date Purchased: _____

Price Paid: _____

Market Value: _____

Purchased At: _____

Moderate

Easy

SPOOKY
the Ghost

BEANIE BABIES
Series I
4090
1998

BEANIE BABIES OFFICIAL CLUB™
SPOOKY
the Ghost
Birthday: 10-31-95
Issued: 9-1-95
Ghosts can be a scary
sight.
But don't let Spooky
bring you any fright
Because when you're
alone, you will see
The best friend that
Spooky can be

LITTLE-KNOWN FACTS:
Spooky the Ghost is one
of only two non-animal
Beanie Babies®. Although
many people think ghosts
are imaginary, they play
important roles in many
religions and cultures
around the world.

4090
©1998 TY INC. BEANIE BABIES OFFICIAL CLUB

Card #
127

Spunky • 4184

SPUNKY
the Cocker Spaniel

BEANIE BABIES
Series I
4184
1998

Moderate

Easy

BEANIE BABIES OFFICIAL CLUB™
SPUNKY
the Cocker Spaniel
Birthday: 1-14-97
Issued: 12-31-97
Bouncing around without
much grace
To jump on your lap and
lick your face
But watch him closely, he
has no fears
He'll run so fast, he'll trip
over his ears!

LITTLE-KNOWN FACTS:
Cocker spaniels are one
of the most popular breeds
of show dogs in the world.
They are also favored as
pets. They are known for
their soft, shiny coats,
and the curly hair on their
ears — called "feathers."

4184
©1998 TY INC. BEANIE BABIES OFFICIAL CLUB

Date Purchased: _____

Price Paid: _____

Market Value: _____

Purchased At: _____

1st Edition

Sting • 4077

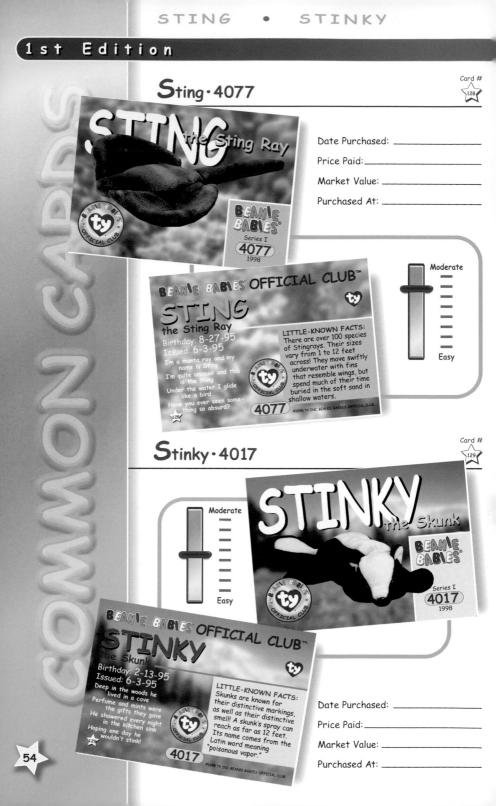

STING
the Sting Ray

BEANIE BABIES
Series I
4077
1998

Date Purchased: _____

Price Paid: _____

Market Value: _____

Purchased At: _____

BEANIE BABIES OFFICIAL CLUB™

STING
the Sting Ray

Birthday: 8-27-95
Issued: 6-3-95

I'm a manta ray and my name is Sting
I'm quite unusual and this is the thing
Under the water I glide like a bird
Have you ever seen something so absurd?

128

4077

LITTLE-KNOWN FACTS:
There are over 100 species of Stingrays. Their sizes vary from 1 to 12 feet across! They move swiftly underwater with fins that resemble wings, but spend much of their time buried in the soft sand in shallow waters.

©1998 TY INC BEANIE BABIES OFFICIAL CLUB

Moderate

Easy

Stinky • 4017

Moderate

Easy

STINKY
the Skunk

BEANIE BABIES
Series I
4017
1998

BEANIE BABIES OFFICIAL CLUB™

STINKY
the Skunk

Birthday: 2-13-95
Issued: 6-3-95

Deep in the woods he lived in a cave
Perfume and mints were the gifts they gave
He showered every night in the kitchen sink
Hoping one day he wouldn't stink!

4017

LITTLE-KNOWN FACTS:
Skunks are known for their distinctive markings, as well as their distinctive smell! A skunk's spray can reach as far as 12 feet. Its name comes from the Latin word meaning "poisonous vapor."

©1998 TY INC BEANIE BABIES OFFICIAL CLUB

Date Purchased: _____

Price Paid: _____

Market Value: _____

Purchased At: _____

COMMON CARDS

COMMON CARDS

Card #
130

Stretch • 4182

Date Purchased: _____

Price Paid: _____

Market Value: _____

Purchased At: _____

Moderate

Easy

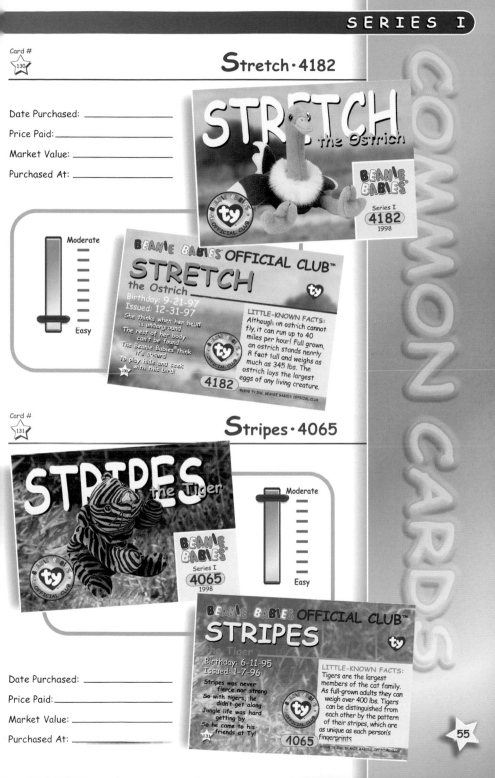

BEANIE BABIES OFFICIAL CLUB™

STRETCH
the Ostrich

Birthday: 9-21-97
Issued: 12-31-97

She thinks when her head
is underground
The rest of her body
can't be found
The Beanie Babies think
it's around
To play hide and seek
with this bird!

4182

LITTLE-KNOWN FACTS:
Although an ostrich cannot
fly, it can run up to 40
miles per hour! Full grown,
an ostrich stands nearly
8 feet tall and weighs as
much as 345 lbs. The
ostrich lays the largest
eggs of any living creature.

©1998 TY INC. BEANIE BABIES OFFICIAL CLUB

Card #
131

Stripes • 4065

Moderate

Easy

BEANIE BABIES OFFICIAL CLUB™
STRIPES
the Tiger

Birthday: 6-11-95
Issued: 1-7-96

Stripes was never
fierce nor strong
So with tigers, he
didn't get along
Jungle life was hard
getting by
So he came to his
friends at Ty!

4065

LITTLE-KNOWN FACTS:
Tigers are the largest
members of the cat family.
As full-grown adults they can
weigh over 400 lbs. Tigers
can be distinguished from
each other by the pattern
of their stripes, which are
as unique as each person's
fingerprints

©1998 TY INC. BEANIE BABIES OFFICIAL CLUB

Date Purchased: _____

Price Paid: _____

Market Value: _____

Purchased At: _____

1st Edition

COMMON CARDS

Tank • 4031

Card #
132

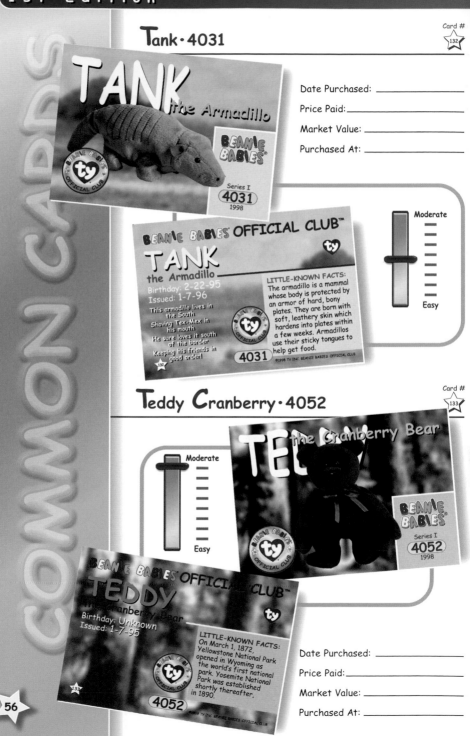

Date Purchased: _____

Price Paid: _____

Market Value: _____

Purchased At: _____

TANK
the Armadillo
Birthday: 2-22-95
Issued: 1-7-96

This armadillo lives in the South
Shoving Tex-Mex in his mouth
He sure loves it south of the border
Keeping his friends in good order!

LITTLE-KNOWN FACTS:
The armadillo is a mammal whose body is protected by an armor of hard, bony plates. They are born with soft, leathery skin which hardens into plates within a few weeks. Armadillos use their sticky tongues to help get food.

4031

©1998 TY INC. BEANIE BABIES OFFICIAL CLUB

Moderate — Easy

Teddy Cranberry • 4052

Card #
133

Moderate — Easy

TEDDY
the Cranberry Bear
Birthday: Unknown
Issued: 1-7-95

LITTLE-KNOWN FACTS:
On March 1, 1872, Yellowstone National Park opened in Wyoming as the world's first national park. Yosemite National Park was established shortly thereafter, in 1890.

4052

Date Purchased: _____

Price Paid: _____

Market Value: _____

Purchased At: _____

COMMON CARDS

Card #
☆ 134

Teddy Jade · 4057

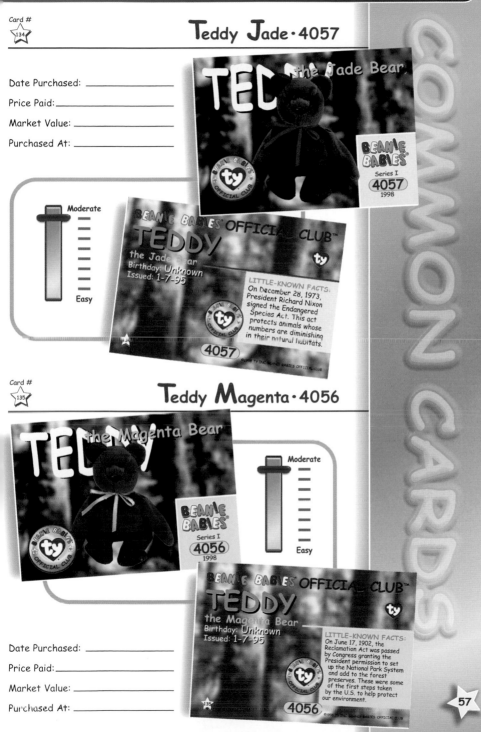

Date Purchased: _____

Price Paid: _____

Market Value: _____

Purchased At: _____

Moderate

Easy

TED the Jade Bear

BEANIE BABIES
Series I
4057
1998

BEANIE BABIES OFFICIAL CLUB
TEDDY
the Jade Bear
Birthday: Unknown
Issued: 1-7-95

LITTLE-KNOWN FACTS:
On December 28, 1973,
President Richard Nixon
signed the Endangered
Species Act. This act
protects animals whose
numbers are diminishing
in their natural habitats.

4057

Card #
☆ 135

Teddy Magenta · 4056

TED the Magenta Bear

BEANIE BABIES
Series I
4056
1998

Moderate

Easy

BEANIE BABIES OFFICIAL CLUB
TEDDY
the Magenta Bear
Birthday: Unknown
Issued: 1-7-95

LITTLE-KNOWN FACTS:
On June 17, 1902, the
Reclamation Act was passed
by Congress granting the
President permission to set
up the National Park System
and add to the forest
preserves. These were some
of the first steps taken
by the U.S. to help protect
our environment.

4056

Date Purchased: _____

Price Paid: _____

Market Value: _____

Purchased At: _____

1st Edition

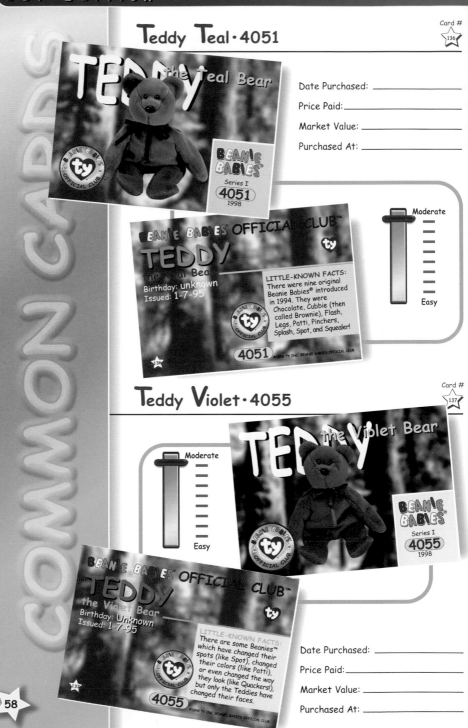

Teddy Teal • 4051

Card #
136

Date Purchased: _____

Price Paid: _____

Market Value: _____

Purchased At: _____

Moderate — Easy

LITTLE-KNOWN FACTS: There were nine original Beanie Babies® introduced in 1994. They were Chocolate, Cubbie (then called Brownie), Flash, Legs, Patti, Pinchers, Splash, Spot, and Squealer!

Teddy Violet • 4055

Card #
137

Moderate — Easy

LITTLE-KNOWN FACTS: There are some Beanies™ which have changed their spots (like Spot), changed their colors (like Patti), or even changed the way they look (like Quackers!), but only the Teddies have changed their faces.

Date Purchased: _____

Price Paid: _____

Market Value: _____

Purchased At: _____

SERIES I

COMMON CARDS

Tracker • 4198

Date Purchased: _____

Price Paid: _____

Market Value: _____

Purchased At: _____

Moderate

Easy

BEANIE BABIES® OFFICIAL CLUB™

TRACKER
the Basset Hound
Birthday: 6-5-97
Issued: 5-30-98

Sniffing and tracking and
following trails
Tracker the basset
always wags his tail
It doesn't matter what
you do
He's always happy when
he's with you!

LITTLE-KNOWN FACTS:
Basset hounds are good
tracking dogs because of
their excellent sense of
smell. This hound will use
its long ears to swirl up
airborne scents into its
very powerful nose.

4198   ©1998 TY INC. BEANIE BABIES OFFICIAL CLUB

Tuffy • 4108

Moderate

Easy

BEANIE BABIES® OFFICIAL CLUB™

TUFFY
the Terrier
Birthday: 10-12-96
Issued: 5-11-97

Taking off with a
thunderous blast
Tuffy rides his
motorcycle fast
The Beanies roll with
laughs & squeals
He never took off his
training wheels!

LITTLE-KNOWN FACTS:
There are over 20 differ-
ent kinds of terriers, most
of which originated in
England. Although they
vary in appearances most
terriers can be identified
by their wiry coats and
the shaggy beards around
their snouts!

4108   ©1998 TY INC. BEANIE BABIES OFFICIAL CLUB

Date Purchased: _____

Price Paid: _____

Market Value: _____

Purchased At: _____

1st Edition

Tusk • 4076

Card #
140

TUSK
the Walrus

BEANIE BABIES
ty OFFICIAL CLUB

Series I
4076
1998

Date Purchased: _____

Price Paid: _____

Market Value: _____

Purchased At: _____

BEANIE BABIES OFFICIAL CLUB™

TUSK
the Walrus

Birthday: 9-18-95
Issued: 1-7-95
Tusk brushes his teeth everyday
To keep them shiny, it's the only way
Teeth are special, so you must try
And they will sparkle when you say "Hi"!

140

LITTLE-KNOWN FACTS:
A walrus has two long teeth called tusks, which are often used as ice picks. These tusks continue to grow for a walrus' entire life, which means they can really get big!

4076
©1998 TY INC. BEANIE BABIES OFFICIAL CLUB

Moderate

Easy

Twigs • 4068

Card #
141

Moderate

Easy

TWIGS
the Giraffe

BEANIE BABIES

Series I
4068
1998

BEANIE BABIES OFFICIAL CLUB™

TWIGS
the Giraffe

Birthday: 5-19-95
Issued: 1-7-96
Twigs has his head in the clouds
He stands tall, he stands proud
With legs so skinny they wobble and shake
What an unusual friend he will make!

141

LITTLE-KNOWN FACTS:
There are nine different species of giraffes — and they all grow up to become the tallest animals in the world. Their long necks allow them to eat food that other animals can't reach. Full-grown, they reach up to 19 feet high!

4068
©1998 TY INC. BEANIE BABIES OFFICIAL CLUB

Date Purchased: _____

Price Paid: _____

Market Value: _____

Purchased At: _____

COMMON CARDS

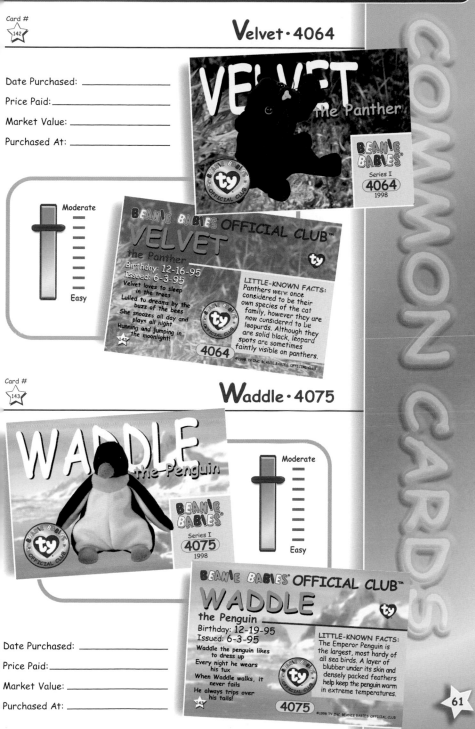

Card #
142

Velvet • 4064

Date Purchased: _____

Price Paid: _____

Market Value: _____

Purchased At: _____

Moderate

Easy

BEANIE BABIES OFFICIAL CLUB™
VELVET
the Panther
Birthday: 12-16-95
Issued: 6-3-95
Velvet loves to sleep in the trees
Lulled to dreams by the buzz of the bees
She snoozes all day and plays all night
Running and jumping in the moonlight!

LITTLE-KNOWN FACTS: Panthers were once considered to be their own species of the cat family, however they are now considered to be leopards. Although they are solid black, leopard spots are sometimes faintly visible on panthers.

4064
©1998 TY INC. BEANIE BABIES OFFICIAL CLUB

Card #
143

Waddle • 4075

Moderate

Easy

Date Purchased: _____

Price Paid: _____

Market Value: _____

Purchased At: _____

BEANIE BABIES OFFICIAL CLUB™
WADDLE
the Penguin
Birthday: 12-19-95
Issued: 6-3-95
Waddle the penguin likes to dress up
Every night he wears his tux
When Waddle walks, it never fails
He always trips over his tails!

LITTLE-KNOWN FACTS: The Emperor Penguin is the largest, most hardy of all sea birds. A layer of blubber under its skin and densely packed feathers help keep the penguin warm in extreme temperatures.

4075
©1998 TY INC BEANIE BABIES OFFICIAL CLUB

61

COMMON CARDS

1st Edition

Waves • 4084

Card # 144

WAVES the Whale

BEANIE BABIES
Series I
4084
1998

Date Purchased: _____

Price Paid: _____

Market Value: _____

Purchased At: _____

BEANIE BABIES OFFICIAL CLUB™
WAVES
the Whale
Birthday: 12-8-96
Issued: 5-11-97
Join him today on the Internet
Don't be afraid to get your feet wet
He taught all the Beanies® how to surf
Our web page is his home turf!
144

LITTLE-KNOWN FACTS:
Waves' cousins, the blue whales, grow up to become the world's largest animals. As a full-grown adult, the blue whale averages 110 ft. in length and 209 tons in weight – that's 418,000 lbs!

4084
©1998 TY INC BEANIE BABIES OFFICIAL CLUB

Moderate
Easy

Weenie • 4013

Card # 145

Moderate
Easy

WEENIE the Dachshund

BEANIE BABIES
Series I
4013
1998

BEANIE BABIES OFFICIAL CLUB™
WEENIE
the Dachshund
Birthday: 7-20-95
Issued: 1-7-96
Weenie the dog is quite a sight
Long of body and short of height
He perches himself high on a log
And considers himself to be Top dog!
145

LITTLE-KNOWN FACTS:
Dachshunds are commonly known as "wiener dogs" because of their long bodies which resemble hot dogs. They come in three different sizes — standard, miniature, and rabbit!

4013
©1998 TY INC BEANIE BABIES OFFICIAL CLUB

Date Purchased: _____

Price Paid: _____

Market Value: _____

Purchased At: _____

COMMON CARDS

COMMON CARDS

Card #
146

Whisper • 4194

Date Purchased: _____

Price Paid: _____

Market Value: _____

Purchased At: _____

WHISPER the Deer

BEANIE BABIES®

Series I
4194
1998

Moderate

Easy

BEANIE BABIES® OFFICIAL CLUB™
WHISPER
the Deer
Birthday: 4-5-97
Issued: 5-30-98

She's very shy as you
can see
When she hides behind
a tree
With big brown eyes and
soft to touch
This little fawn will love
you so much!

4194

LITTLE-KNOWN FACTS:
The white tail deer is
found across much of
North America. Their
coats often change from
brown to gray with the
seasons to match their
surroundings. Young deer,
or fawns are born with a
tan coat with white spots.

©1998 TY INC. BEANIE BABIES OFFICIAL CLUB

Card #
147

Wrinkles • 4103

WRINKLES the Bulldog

BEANIE BABIES®

Series I
4103
1998

Moderate

Easy

BEANIE BABIES® OFFICIAL CLUB™
WRINKLES
the Bulldog
Birthday: 5-1-96
Issued: 6-15-96

This little dog is named
Wrinkles
His nose is soft and often
crinkles
Likes to climb up on your
lap
He's a cheery sort of
chap!

4103

LITTLE-KNOWN FACTS:
Originally raised in England,
bulldogs are noted for
their even temperment,
and make excellent pets.
Bulldogs are also known
to snore louder than any
other breed of dogs!

©1998 TY INC. BEANIE BABIES OFFICIAL CLUB

Date Purchased: _____

Price Paid: _____

Market Value: _____

Purchased At: _____

63

COMMON CARDS

Ziggy • 4063

Card # 148

ZIGGY the Zebra

BEANIE BABIES®
ty OFFICIAL CLUB

Series I
4063
1998

Date Purchased: _____

Price Paid: _____

Market Value: _____

Purchased At: _____

BEANIE BABIES® OFFICIAL CLUB™
ZIGGY
the Zebra
Birthday: 12-24-95
Issued: 6-3-95

Ziggy likes soccer-he's a referee
That way he watches the games for free
The other Beanies don't think it's fair
But Ziggy the Zebra doesn't care!

LITTLE-KNOWN FACTS:
Baby zebras are called *foals*, and weigh up to 75 lbs. at birth. When it grows up, an adult zebra will spend 60-80 percent of its time eating! When grass is scarce during the dry season, zebras search for food together.
©1998 TY INC BEANIE BABIES OFFICIAL CLUB

4063

Moderate —— Easy

Zip • 4004

Card # 149

Moderate —— Easy

ZIP the Cat with the white face

BEANIE BABIES®
ty OFFICIAL CLUB

Series I
4004
1998

BEANIE BABIES® OFFICIAL CLUB™
ZIP
the Cat
Birthday: 3-28-94
Issued: 1-7-95

Keep Zip by your side all the day through
Zip is good luck; you'll see it's true
When you have something you need to do
Zip will always believe in you!

LITTLE-KNOWN FACTS:
A cat's fur helps regulate its body temperature. When it's cold, their fur protects them from the weather. When it's hot, a cat can raise its fur in order to allow cool air to circulate underneath.
©1998 TY INC BEANIE BABIES OFFICIAL CLUB

4004

Date Purchased: _____

Price Paid: _____

Market Value: _____

Purchased At: _____

The Birthday/Rookie Cards

The first of the chaser card subsets in Series I, the Birthday/Rookie cards display the same high standard of quality design and production as do the Common cards, but with their own unique twist.

The front of each Birthday/Rookie card shows a Beanie, its name, its birthday, and the Official Club logo. Each card displays a softly blurred, full-color natural background, with a sharper and more detailed image of the Beanie in the foreground.

The name of each Birthday Beanie has been foil stamped and printed in one of four rich, glossy colors: red blend, blue blend, silver, and gold. (Some cards are also stamped with "ROOKIE" in gold). The color of the foil name determines the level of rarity of that particular card. The easiest variation to find in this subgroup is red, then blue, silver, and finally, the most difficult variation to find, gold. Each gold level card is crash-numbered 1 of a limited amount, adding an additional level of rarity.

The back of the card, also depicting the Beanie in full color, shows issue dates, series number, and the Beanie Baby's poem. There are 25 Birthday cards in Series I, numbered 25 to 49, and the odds of finding a Birthday card are 1 in 2 packs.

BIRTHDAY CARDS

Ants · 4195

Card #
25

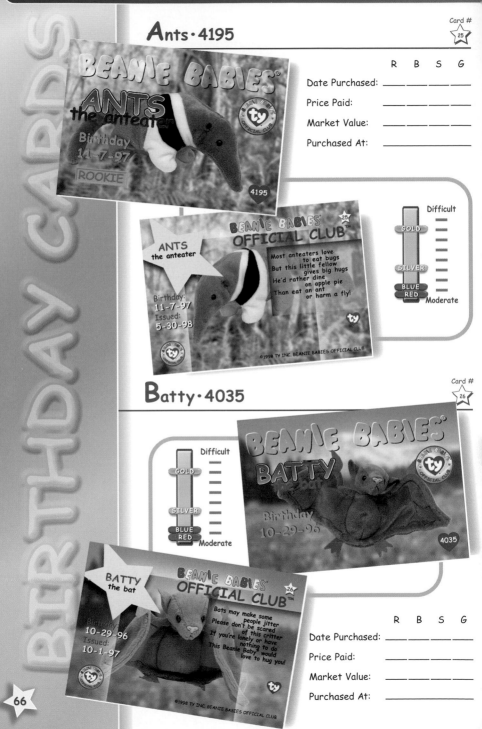

BEANIE BABIES®
ANTS
the anteater
Birthday
11-7-97
ROOKIE
4195

	R	B	S	G
Date Purchased:				
Price Paid:				
Market Value:				
Purchased At:				

BEANIE BABIES®
OFFICIAL CLUB™
25

ANTS
the anteater

Birthday:
11-7-97
Issued:
5-30-98

Most anteaters love
to eat bugs
But this little fellow
gives big hugs
He'd rather dine
on apple pie
Than eat an ant
or harm a fly!

ty

©1998 TY INC. BEANIE BABIES OFFICIAL CLUB

Difficult
GOLD
SILVER
BLUE
RED
Moderate

Batty · 4035

Card #
26

Difficult
GOLD
SILVER
BLUE
RED
Moderate

BEANIE BABIES®
BATTY
the bat
Birthday
10-29-96
4035

BEANIE BABIES®
OFFICIAL CLUB™
26

BATTY
the bat

Birthday:
10-29-96
Issued:
10-1-97

Bats may make some
people jitter
Please don't be scared
of this critter
If you're lonely or have
nothing to do
This Beanie Baby would
love to hug you!

ty

©1998 TY INC. BEANIE BABIES OFFICIAL CLUB

	R	B	S	G
Date Purchased:				
Price Paid:				
Market Value:				
Purchased At:				

SERIES I

BIRTHDAY CARDS

Card #
27

Bessie • 4009

R   B   S   G

Date Purchased: _____

Price Paid: _____

Market Value: _____

Purchased At: _____

BEANIE BABIES
BESSIE
the cow
Birthday
6-27-95
4009

Difficult

GOLD

SILVER

BLUE
RED

Moderate

BEANIE BABIES
OFFICIAL CLUB

BESSIE
the cow

Birthday:
6-27-95
Issued:
6-3-95

27

Bessie the cow likes
to dance and sing
Because music is her
favorite thing
Every night when you
are counting sheep
She'll sing you a song
to help you sleep!

© 1998 TY INC. BEANIE BABIES OFFICIAL CLUB

Card #
28

Bubbles • 4078

BEANIE BABIES
BUBBLES
the fish
Birthday
7-2-95
4078

Difficult

GOLD

SILVER

BLUE
RED

Moderate

R   B   S   G

Date Purchased: _____

Price Paid: _____

Market Value: _____

Purchased At: _____

BUBBLES
the fish

Birthday:
7-2-95
Issued:
6-3-95

BEANIE BABIES
OFFICIAL CLUB

28

All day long Bubbles
likes to swim
She never gets tired
flapping her fins
Bubbles lived in
a sea of blue
Now she is ready to come
home with you!

© 1998 TY INC. BEANIE BABIES OFFICIAL CLUB

BIRTHDAY CARDS

Bucky · 4016

Card #
29

	R	B	S	G
Date Purchased:				
Price Paid:				
Market Value:				
Purchased At:				

BUCKY the beaver
Birthday 6-8-95

BEANIE BABIES
BUCKY the beaver
Birthday: 6-8-95
Issued: 1-7-96

BEANIE BABIES OFFICIAL CLUB™
Bucky's teeth are shiny as can be
Often used for cutting trees
He hides in his dam night and day
Maybe for you he will come out and play!
©1998 TY INC. BEANIE BABIES OFFICIAL CLUB

Difficult
GOLD
SILVER
BLUE
RED
Moderate

Clubby

Card #
30

Difficult
GOLD
SILVER
BLUE
RED
Moderate

CLUBBY the bear
Birthday 7-7-98
ROOKIE

BEANIE BABIES
CLUBBY the bear

CLUBBY the bear
Birthday: 7-7-98

BEANIE BABIES OFFICIAL CLUB™
Wearing his club pin for all to see
He's a proud member like you and me
Made especially with you in mind
Clubby the bear is one of a kind!
©1998 TY INC. BEANIE BABIES OFFICIAL CLUB

	R	B	S	G
Date Purchased:				
Price Paid:				
Market Value:				
Purchased At:				

68

Card #
31

Crunch · 4130

R B S G

Date Purchased: ___ ___ ___ ___

Price Paid: ___ ___ ___ ___

Market Value: ___ ___ ___ ___

Purchased At: _____

Difficult

GOLD

SILVER

BLUE
RED

Moderate

BEANIE BABIES
CRUNCH
the shark
Birthday
1-13-96
4130

CRUNCH
the shark
Birthday:
1-13-96
Issued:
1-1-97

BEANIE BABIES OFFICIAL CLUB

What's for breakfast?
What's for lunch?
Yum! Delicious! Munch,
munch, munch!
He's eating everything
by the bunch
That's the reason we named
him Crunch!

©1998 TY INC. BEANIE BABIES OFFICIAL CLUB

Card #
32

Erin · 4186

BEANIE BABIES
ERIN
the bear
Birthday
3-17-97
ROOKIE
4186

Difficult

GOLD

SILVER

BLUE
RED

Moderate

ERIN
the bear
Birthday
3-17-97
Issued:
1-31-98

BEANIE BABIES OFFICIAL CLUB

Named after the beautiful
Emerald Isle
This Beanie Baby will
make you smile
A bit of luck, a pot
of gold
Light up the faces, both
young and old!

©1998 TY INC. BEANIE BABIES OFFICIAL CLUB

R B S G

Date Purchased: ___ ___ ___ ___

Price Paid: ___ ___ ___ ___

Market Value: ___ ___ ___ ___

Purchased At: _____

BIRTHDAY CARDS

69

1st Edition

Fetch · 4189

R B S G

Date Purchased: _____

Price Paid: _____

Market Value: _____

Purchased At: _____

BEANIE BABIES
FETCH
the golden retriever
Birthday
2-4-97
ROOKIE
4189

BEANIE BABIES
OFFICIAL CLUB™
33
FETCH
the golden retriever
Fetch is alert at the
crack of dawn
Walking through dew
drops on the lawn
Always golden, loyal
and true
This little puppy is
the one for you!
Birthday:
2-4-97
Issued:
5-30-98
©1998 TY INC BEANIE BABIES OFFICIAL CLUB

Difficult
GOLD
SILVER
BLUE
RED
Moderate

Fortune · 4196

Difficult
GOLD
SILVER
BLUE
RED
Moderate

BEANIE BABIES
FORTUNE
the panda
Birthday
12-6-97
ROOKIE
4196

BEANIE BABIES
OFFICIAL CLUB™
34
FORTUNE
the panda
Nibbling on a
bamboo tree
This little panda
is hard to see
You're so lucky with this
one you found
Only a few are
still around!
Birthday:
12-6-97
Issued:
5-30-98
©1998 TY INC BEANIE BABIES OFFICIAL CLUB

R B S G

Date Purchased: _____

Price Paid: _____

Market Value: _____

Purchased At: _____

BIRTHDAY CARDS

BIRTHDAY CARDS

Card #
35

Glory · 4188

R   B   S   G

Date Purchased: _____ ___ ___ ___

Price Paid: ___ ___ ___ ___

Market Value: ___ ___ ___ ___

Purchased At: _____

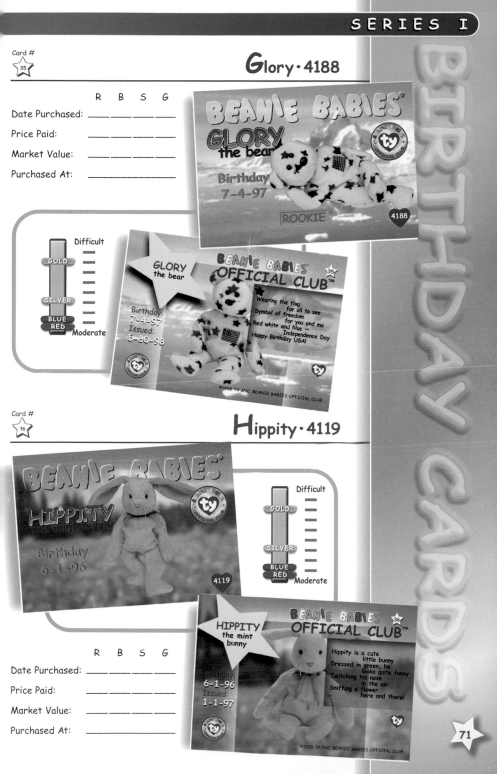

BEANIE BABIES®
GLORY
the bear
Birthday
7-4-97
ROOKIE
4188

Difficult
GOLD
SILVER
BLUE
RED
Moderate

GLORY
the bear
Birthday:
7-4-97
Issued:
5-30-98

BEANIE BABIES®
OFFICIAL CLUB™
35

Wearing the flag
for all to see
Symbol of freedom
for you and me
Red white and blue —
Independence Day
Happy Birthday USA!

©1998 TY INC. BEANIE BABIES OFFICIAL CLUB

Card #
36

Hippity · 4119

BEANIE BABIES®
HIPPITY
the mint bunny
Birthday
6-1-96
4119

Difficult
GOLD
SILVER
BLUE
RED
Moderate

R   B   S   G

Date Purchased: _____ ___ ___ ___

Price Paid: ___ ___ ___ ___

Market Value: ___ ___ ___ ___

Purchased At: _____

HIPPITY
the mint
bunny
Birthday:
6-1-96
Issued:
1-1-97

BEANIE BABIES®
OFFICIAL CLUB™
36

Hippity is a cute
little bunny
Dressed in green, he
looks quite funny
Twitching his nose
in the air
Sniffing a flower
here and there!

©1998 TY INC. BEANIE BABIES OFFICIAL CLUB

71

1st Edition

Kiwi • 4070

Card #
37

BEANIE BABIES
KIWI
the toucan
Birthday
9-16-95
4070

	R	B	S	G
Date Purchased:				
Price Paid:				
Market Value:				
Purchased At:				

37
BEANIE BABIES
OFFICIAL CLUB

KIWI
the toucan

Kiwi waits for
April showers
Watching a garden bloom
with flowers
There trees grow with fruit
that's sweet
I'm sure you'll guess his
favorite treat!

Birthday:
9-16-95
Issued:
6-3-95

©1998 TY INC. BEANIE BABIES OFFICIAL CLUB

Difficult
GOLD
SILVER
BLUE
RED
Moderate

Lizzy • 4033

Card #
38

Difficult
GOLD
SILVER
BLUE
RED
Moderate

BEANIE BABIES
LIZZY
the tie-dyed lizard
Birthday
5-11-95
4033

30
BEANIE BABIES
OFFICIAL CLUB

LIZZY
the tie-dyed
lizard

Birthday:
5-11-95
Issued:
6-3-95

Lizzy loves Legs
the frog
She hides with
him under logs
Both of them search
for flies
Underneath the clear
blue skies.

©1998 TY INC. BEANIE BABIES OFFICIAL CLUB

	R	B	S	G
Date Purchased:				
Price Paid:				
Market Value:				
Purchased At:				

BIRTHDAY CARDS

Card #
39

Mel · 4162

	R	B	S	G
Date Purchased:				
Price Paid:				
Market Value:				
Purchased At:				

Difficult
GOLD
SILVER
BLUE
RED
Moderate

MEL
the koala

Birthday:
1-15-96
Issued:
1-1-97

BEANIE BABIES
OFFICIAL CLUB™

39

How do you name
a Koala bear?
It's rather tough,
I do declare!
It confuses me
I get into a funk
I'll name him Mel, after my
favorite hunk!

©1998 TY INC. BEANIE BABIES OFFICIAL CLUB

Card #
40

Nanook · 4104

BEANIE BABIES®

NANOOK
the husky

Birthday
11-21-96

4104

Difficult
GOLD
SILVER
BLUE
RED
Moderate

NANOOK
the husky

Birthday:
11-21-96
Issued:
5-11-97

BEANIE BABIES®
OFFICIAL CLUB™

40

Nanook is a dog that
loves cold weather
To him a sled is
light as a feather
Over the snow and
through the slush
He runs at hearing
the cry of "mush!"

©1998 TY INC. BEANIE BABIES OFFICIAL CLUB

	R	B	S	G
Date Purchased:				
Price Paid:				
Market Value:				
Purchased At:				

1st Edition

Nip · 4003

	R	B	S	G
Date Purchased:				
Price Paid:				
Market Value:				
Purchased At:				

NIP
the gold cat with white paws
Birthday: 3-6-94
Issued: 3-10-96

His name is Nipper,
but we call him Nip
His best friend is a black cat
named Zip
Nip likes to run in races
for fun
He runs so fast he's
always number one!

©1998 TY INC. BEANIE BABIES OFFICIAL CLUB

Pinky · 4072

PINKY
the flamingo
Birthday: 2-13-95
Issued: 6-3-95

Pinky loves
the everglades
From the hottest pink
she's made
With floppy legs
and big orange beak
She's the Beanie™
that you seek!

©1998 TY INC. BEANIE BABIES OFFICIAL CLUB

	R	B	S	G
Date Purchased:				
Price Paid:				
Market Value:				
Purchased At:				

BIRTHDAY CARDS

BIRTHDAY CARDS

Card #
43

Princess · 4300

	R	B	S	G
Date Purchased:	__ __ __ __
Price Paid:	__ __ __ __
Market Value:	__ __ __ __
Purchased At:	_____

Difficult

GOLD

SILVER

BLUE
RED

Moderate

PRINCESS
the bear

ROOKIE

4300

PRINCESS
the bear

Issued:
10-29-97

BEANIE BABIES
OFFICIAL CLUB™

Like an angel, she came
from heaven above
She shared her compassion,
her pain, her love
She only stayed with us long
enough to teach
The world to share,
to give, to reach

©1998 TY INC. BEANIE BABIES OFFICIAL CLUB

Card #
44

Radar · 4091

BEANIE BABIES
RADAR
the bat

Birthday
10-30-95

4091

Difficult

GOLD

SILVER

BLUE
RED

Moderate

RADAR
the bat

Birthday:
10-30-95
Issued:
9-1-95

BEANIE BABIES
OFFICIAL CLUB™

Radar the bat
flies late at night
He can soar to
an amazing height
If you see something
as high as a star
Take a good look,
it might be Radar!

©1998 TY INC. BEANIE BABIES OFFICIAL CLUB

	R	B	S	G
Date Purchased:	__ __ __ __
Price Paid:	__ __ __ __
Market Value:	__ __ __ __
Purchased At:	_____

1st Edition

Scoop · 4107

Card #
45

BEANIE BABIES®
SCOOP
the pelican
Birthday
7-1-96
4107

	R	B	S	G
Date Purchased:				
Price Paid:				
Market Value:				
Purchased At:				

BEANIE BABIES
OFFICIAL CLUB™
45

SCOOP
the pelican

Birthday:
7-1-96
Issued:
6-15-96

All day long he scoops up fish
To fill his bill, is his wish
Diving fast and diving low
Hoping those fish are very slow!

©1998 TY INC. BEANIE BABIES OFFICIAL CLUB

Difficult
GOLD
SILVER
BLUE
RED
Moderate

Stinger · 4193

Card #
46

Difficult
GOLD
SILVER
BLUE
RED
Moderate

BEANIE BABIES®
STINGER
the scorpion
Birthday
9-29-97
4193
ROOKIE

BEANIE BABIES
OFFICIAL CLUB™
46

STINGER
the scorpion

Birthday:
9-29-97
Issued:
5-30-98

Stinger the scorpion
will run and dart
But this little fellow
is really all heart
So if you see him
don't run away
Say hello and
ask him to play!

©1998 TY INC. BEANIE BABIES OFFICIAL CLUB

	R	B	S	G
Date Purchased:				
Price Paid:				
Market Value:				
Purchased At:				

BIRTHDAY CARDS

Card # 47

Strut · 4171

	R	B	S	G
Date Purchased:	___ ___ ___ ___
Price Paid:	___ ___ ___ ___
Market Value:	___ ___ ___ ___
Purchased At:	_____

BEANIE BABIES
STRUT
the rooster
Birthday
3-8-96
4171

Difficult
GOLD
SILVER
BLUE
RED
Moderate

STRUT
the rooster

BEANIE BABIES
OFFICIAL CLUB
47

Birthday:
3-8-96
Issued:
7-12-97

Listen closely to
"Cock-a-doodle-doo"
What's the rooster
saying to you?
Hurry, wake up
sleepy head
We have lots to do,
get out of bed!

©1998 TY INC. BEANIE BABIES OFFICIAL CLUB

Card # 48

Tabasco · 4002

BEANIE BABIES
TABASCO
the bull
Birthday
5-15-95
4002

Difficult
GOLD
SILVER
BLUE
RED
Moderate

TABASCO
the bull

BEANIE BABIES
OFFICIAL CLUB
48

Birthday:
5-15-95
Issued:
6-3-95

Although Tabasco
is not so tall
He loves to play
basketball
He is a star player
in his dream
Can you guess
his favorite team?

©1998 TY INC. BEANIE BABIES OFFICIAL CLUB

	R	B	S	G
Date Purchased:	___ ___ ___ ___
Price Paid:	___ ___ ___ ___
Market Value:	___ ___ ___ ___
Purchased At:	_____

BIRTHDAY CARDS

BIRTHDAY CARDS

Valentino • 4058

Card #
49

BEANIE BABIES
VALENTINO
the bear
Birthday
2-14-94
4058

	R	B	S	G
Date Purchased:				
Price Paid:				
Market Value:				
Purchased At:				

BEANIE BABIES
OFFICIAL CLUB
49
VALENTINO
the bear

Birthday:
2-14-94
Issued:
1-7-95

His heart is red
and full of love
He cares for you
so give him a hug
Keep him close
when feeling blue
Feel the love,
he has for you!

©1998 TY INC BEANIE BABIES OFFICIAL CLUB

Difficult
GOLD
SILVER
BLUE
RED
Moderate

78

The Retired Cards

The Retired cards showcase a variety of retired Beanies. The quality and originality of the cards in this card subset reflects their level of rarity.

The front of each Retired card shows a Beanie, its name, retired date, and style number. The image of the beanie has been printed on a holographic foil board background. When moved under light, this rich background produces flashes of metallic color that contrast with the solid color of the Beanie in the foreground for an animated effect.

The name of each Beanie appears in a double foiled and embossed stamp. Each Beanie's retired date is shown on the front of these cards as a foil stamp. As with the Birthday cards, the color of this embossed stamp determines the level of rarity of that particular card. The same four levels of color are used here: red, blue, silver, and gold, with gold being the most difficult variation to find. Each gold level card is crash-numbered 1 of a limited amount, adding an additional level of collectibility.

The back of each card shows issue, birth, and retired dates and little-known facts. There are 15 Retired cards in Series I, numbered 10 to 24. The odds of finding a Retired card are 1 in 7 packs.

RETIRED CARDS

79

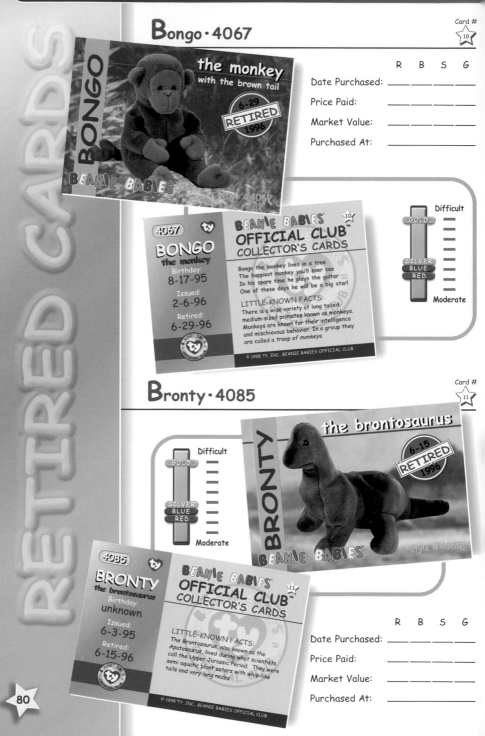

Bongo • 4067

Card #
10

	R	B	S	G
Date Purchased:				
Price Paid:				
Market Value:				
Purchased At:				

4067 ty

BONGO
the monkey
Birthday:
8-17-95

Issued:
2-6-96

Retired:
6-29-96

BEANIE BABIES® OFFICIAL CLUB™ COLLECTOR'S CARDS
10

Bongo the monkey lives in a tree
The happiest monkey you'll ever see
In his spare time he plays the guitar
One of these days he will be a big star!

LITTLE-KNOWN FACTS:
There is a wide variety of long tailed,
medium-sized primates known as monkeys.
Monkeys are known for their intelligence
and mischievous behavior. In a group they
are called a *troop of monkeys*.

© 1998 TY, INC., BEANIE BABIES OFFICIAL CLUB

Difficult
GOLD
SILVER
BLUE
RED
Moderate

Bronty • 4085

Card #
11

Difficult
GOLD
SILVER
BLUE
RED
Moderate

4085 ty

BRONTY
the brontosaurus
Birthday:
unknown

Issued:
6-3-95

Retired:
6-15-96

BEANIE BABIES® OFFICIAL CLUB™ COLLECTOR'S CARDS
11

LITTLE-KNOWN FACTS:
The Brontosaurus, also known as the
Apatosaurus, lived during what scientists
call the Upper Jurassic Period. They were
semi aquatic plant eaters with tails and very long necks.

© 1998 TY, INC., BEANIE BABIES OFFICIAL CLUB

	R	B	S	G
Date Purchased:				
Price Paid:				
Market Value:				
Purchased At:				

Chilly · 4012

Card #
12

	R	B	S	G
Date Purchased:				
Price Paid:				
Market Value:				
Purchased At:				

CHILLY
the polar bear
1-7
RETIRED
1996
style #4012
BEANIE BABIES

Difficult
GOLD
SILVER
BLUE
RED
Moderate

4012 ty
CHILLY
the polar bear
Birthday:
unknown
Issued:
6-25-94
Retired:
1-7-96

BEANIE BABIES
OFFICIAL CLUB
COLLECTOR'S CARDS

LITTLE-KNOWN FACTS:
Polar bears are the largest of all bears.
Males can be 8-11 feet tall and weigh as
much as 1,000 lbs. They actually have
black skin under their fur. Their black
noses are a clue!

© 1998 TY, INC. BEANIE BABIES OFFICIAL CLUB

Goldie · 4023

Card #
13

GOLDIE
the goldfish
12-31
RETIRED
1997
style #4023
BEANIE BABIES

Difficult
GOLD
SILVER
BLUE
RED
Moderate

4023 ty
GOLDIE
the goldfish
Birthday:
11-14-94
Issued:
6-25-94
Retired:
12-31-97

BEANIE BABIES
OFFICIAL CLUB
COLLECTOR'S CARDS

She's got rhythm, she's got soul
What more to like in a fish bowl?
Through sound waves Goldie swam
Because this goldfish likes to jam!

LITTLE-KNOWN FACTS:
A goldfish is a colorful, freshwater fish
similar to a carp. They were native to
Europe and Asia but are now common
worldwide as ornamental fish. When they
are young, goldfish are brownish in color,
but become brighter as they mature.

© 1998 TY, INC. BEANIE BABIES OFFICIAL CLUB

	R	B	S	G
Date Purchased:				
Price Paid:				
Market Value:				
Purchased At:				

RETIRED CARDS

Humphrey · 4060

Card #
14

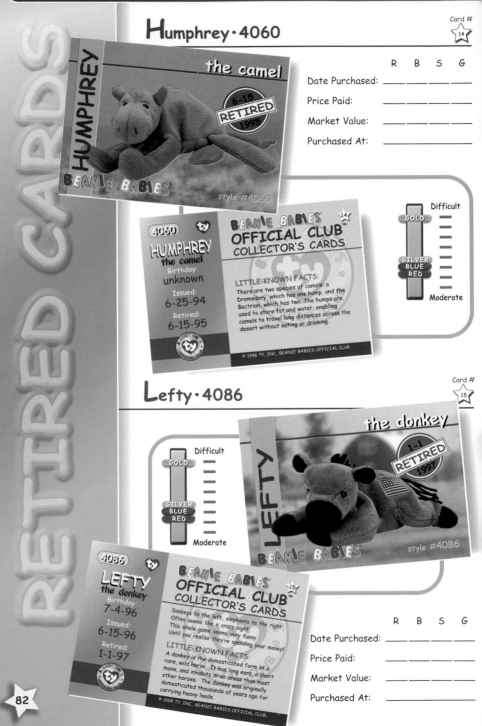

HUMPHREY

the camel

6-15
RETIRED
1995

HUMPHREY

BEANIE BABIES

style #4060

	R	B	S	G
Date Purchased:				
Price Paid:				
Market Value:				
Purchased At:				

4060 ty

HUMPHREY
the camel
Birthday:
unknown
Issued:
6-25-94
Retired:
6-15-95

BEANIE BABIES
OFFICIAL CLUB
COLLECTOR'S CARDS

LITTLE-KNOWN FACTS:
There are two species of camels: a
Dromedary, which has one hump, and the
Bactrian, which has two. The humps are
used to store fat and water, enabling
camels to travel long distances across the
desert without eating or drinking.

© 1998 TY, INC., BEANIE BABIES OFFICIAL CLUB

Difficult
GOLD
SILVER
BLUE
RED
Moderate

Lefty · 4086

Card #
15

Difficult
GOLD
SILVER
BLUE
RED
Moderate

the donkey

1-1
RETIRED
1997

LEFTY

BEANIE BABIES

style #4086

4086 ty

LEFTY
the donkey
Birthday:
7-4-96
Issued:
6-15-96
Retired:
1-1-97

BEANIE BABIES
OFFICIAL CLUB
COLLECTOR'S CARDS

Donkeys to the left, elephants to the right
Often seems like a crazy sight
This whole game seems very funny
Until you realize they're spending your money!

LITTLE-KNOWN FACTS:
A donkey is the domesticated form of a
rare, wild horse. It has long ears, a short
mane, and inhabits drier areas than most
other horses. The donkey was originally
domesticated thousands of years ago for
carrying heavy loads.

© 1998 TY, INC., BEANIE BABIES OFFICIAL CLUB.

	R	B	S	G
Date Purchased:				
Price Paid:				
Market Value:				
Purchased At:				

RETIRED CARDS

Peanut · 4062

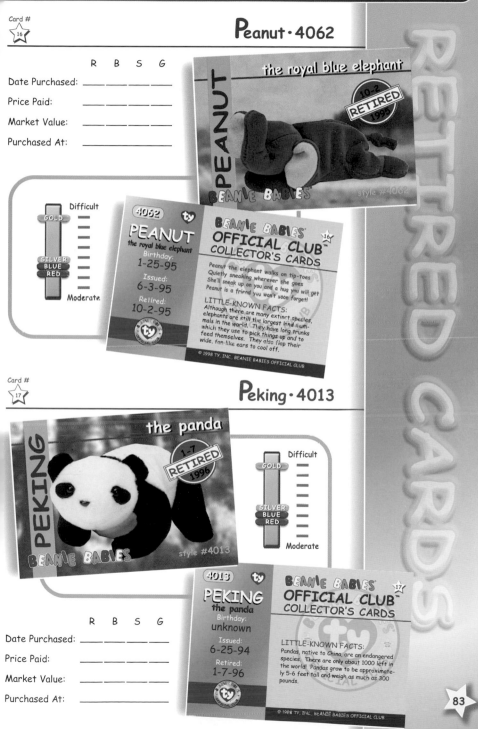

the royal blue elephant

PEANUT

RETIRED 10-2 1995

BEANIE BABIES

style #4062

R B S G

Date Purchased: _____

Price Paid: _____

Market Value: _____

Purchased At: _____

Difficult

GOLD

SILVER
BLUE
RED

Moderate

4062 ty

PEANUT
the royal blue elephant

Birthday:
1-25-95

Issued:
6-3-95

Retired:
10-2-95

BEANIE BABIES
OFFICIAL CLUB
COLLECTOR'S CARDS

16

Peanut the elephant walks on tip-toes
Quietly sneaking wherever she goes
She'll sneak up on you and a hug you will get
Peanut is a friend you won't soon forget!

LITTLE-KNOWN FACTS:
Although there are many extinct species,
elephants are still the largest land mammals in the world. They have long trunks
which they use to pick things up and to
feed themselves. They also flap their
wide, fan-like ears to cool off.

© 1998 TY, INC., BEANIE BABIES OFFICIAL CLUB

Peking · 4013

the panda

PEKING

RETIRED 1-7 1996

BEANIE BABIES

style #4013

Difficult

GOLD

SILVER
BLUE
RED

Moderate

4013 ty

PEKING
the panda

Birthday:
unknown

Issued:
6-25-94

Retired:
1-7-96

BEANIE BABIES
OFFICIAL CLUB
COLLECTOR'S CARDS

17

LITTLE-KNOWN FACTS:
Pandas, native to China, are an endangered
species. There are only about 1000 left in
the world! Pandas grow to be approximately 5-6 feet tall and weigh as much as 300
pounds.

© 1998 TY, INC., BEANIE BABIES OFFICIAL CLUB

R B S G

Date Purchased: _____

Price Paid: _____

Market Value: _____

Purchased At: _____

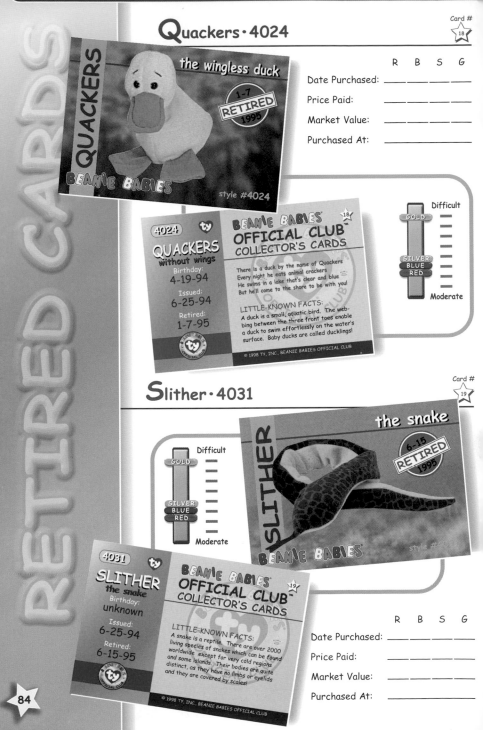

Quackers • 4024

Card # 18

R B S G

Date Purchased: _____
Price Paid: _____
Market Value: _____
Purchased At: _____

Slither • 4031

Card # 19

R B S G

Date Purchased: _____
Price Paid: _____
Market Value: _____
Purchased At: _____

84

Card #
20

Steg · 4087

R B S G

Date Purchased: ___ ___ ___ ___

Price Paid: ___ ___ ___ ___

Market Value: ___ ___ ___ ___

Purchased At: ___ ___ ___ ___

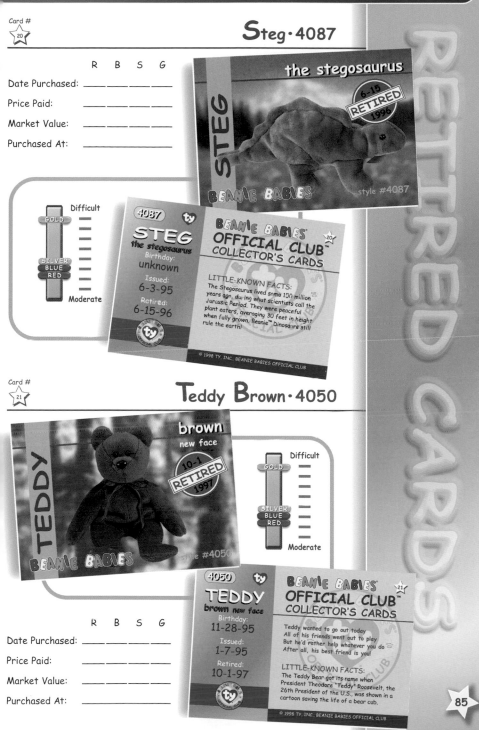

the stegosaurus

STEG

6-15
RETIRED
1996

BEANIE BABIES

style #4087

Difficult

GOLD

SILVER
BLUE
RED

Moderate

4087 ty

STEG
the stegosaurus

Birthday:
unknown

Issued:
6-3-95

Retired:
6-15-96

BEANIE BABIES
OFFICIAL CLUB
COLLECTOR'S CARDS

20

LITTLE-KNOWN FACTS:
The Stegosaurus lived some 150 million
years ago, during what scientists call the
Jurassic Period. They were peaceful
plant eaters, averaging 30 feet in height
when fully grown. Beanie™ Dinosaurs still
rule the earth!

© 1998 TY, INC. BEANIE BABIES OFFICIAL CLUB

Card #
21

Teddy Brown · 4050

brown
new face

TEDDY

10-1
RETIRED
1997

BEANIE BABIES

style #4050

Difficult

GOLD

SILVER
BLUE
RED

Moderate

4050 ty

TEDDY
brown new face

Birthday:
11-28-95

Issued:
1-7-95

Retired:
10-1-97

BEANIE BABIES
OFFICIAL CLUB
COLLECTOR'S CARDS

21

Teddy wanted to go out today
All of his friends went out to play
But he'd rather help whatever you do
After all, his best friend is you!

LITTLE-KNOWN FACTS:
The Teddy Bear got its name when
President Theodore "Teddy" Roosevelt, the
26th President of the U.S., was shown in a
cartoon saving the life of a bear cub.

© 1998 TY, INC. BEANIE BABIES OFFICIAL CLUB

R B S G

Date Purchased: ___ ___ ___ ___

Price Paid: ___ ___ ___ ___

Market Value: ___ ___ ___ ___

Purchased At: ___ ___ ___ ___

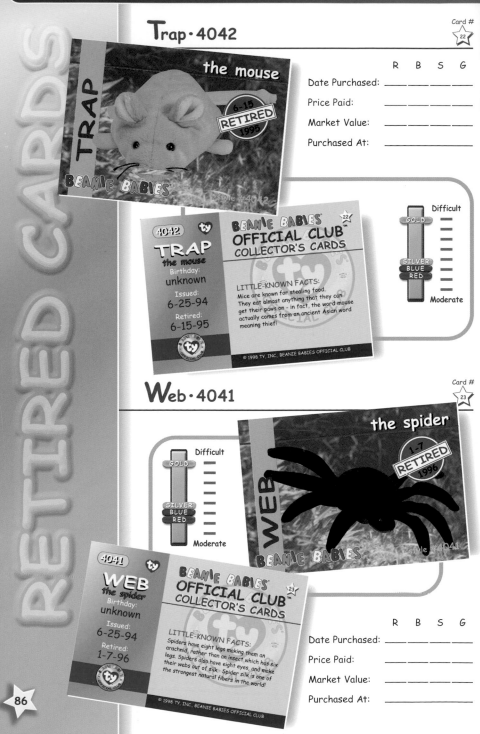

RETIRED CARDS

Trap • 4042

Card #
22

R   B   S   G

Date Purchased: _____

Price Paid: _____

Market Value: _____

Purchased At: _____

4042 ty
TRAP
the mouse
Birthday:
unknown
Issued:
6-25-94
Retired:
6-15-95

BEANIE BABIES
OFFICIAL CLUB
COLLECTOR'S CARDS
22

LITTLE-KNOWN FACTS:
Mice are known for stealing food.
They eat almost anything that they can
get their paws on - in fact, the word mouse
actually comes from an ancient Asian word
meaning thief!

© 1998 TY, INC., BEANIE BABIES OFFICIAL CLUB

Difficult
GOLD
SILVER
BLUE
RED
Moderate

Web • 4041

Card #
23

Difficult
GOLD
SILVER
BLUE
RED
Moderate

4041 ty
WEB
the spider
Birthday:
unknown
Issued:
6-25-94
Retired:
1-7-96

BEANIE BABIES
OFFICIAL CLUB
COLLECTOR'S CARDS
23

LITTLE-KNOWN FACTS:
Spiders have eight legs making them an
arachnid, rather than an insect which has six
legs. Spiders also have eight eyes, and make
their webs out of silk. Spider silk is one of
the strongest natural fibers in the world!

© 1998 TY, INC., BEANIE BABIES OFFICIAL CLUB

R   B   S   G

Date Purchased: _____

Price Paid: _____

Market Value: _____

Purchased At: _____

Card #
⭐ 24

Zip · 4004

R B S G

Date Purchased: ___ ___ ___ ___

Price Paid: ___ ___ ___ ___

Market Value: ___ ___ ___ ___

Purchased At: _____

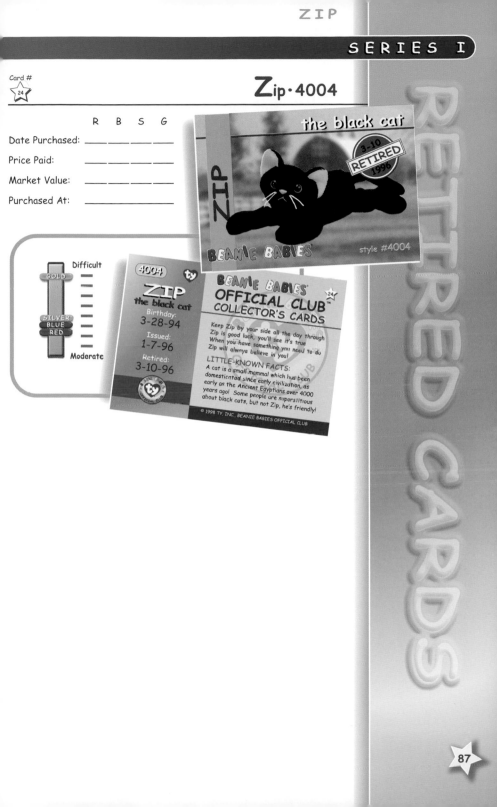

the black cat

ZIP

3-10
RETIRED
1996

BEANIE BABIES

style #4004

Difficult

GOLD

SILVER
BLUE
RED

Moderate

4004 ty

ZIP
the black cat
Birthday:
3-28-94
Issued:
1-7-96
Retired:
3-10-96

24

BEANIE BABIES®
OFFICIAL CLUB™
COLLECTOR'S CARDS

Keep Zip by your side all the day through
Zip is good luck, you'll see it's true
When you have something you need to do
Zip will always believe in you!

LITTLE-KNOWN FACTS:
A cat is a small mammal which has been
domesticated since early civilization, as
early as the Ancient Egyptians over 4000
years ago! Some people are superstitious
about black cats, but not Zip, he's friendly!

© 1998 TY, INC., BEANIE BABIES OFFICIAL CLUB

RETIRED CARDS

The Original 9

The last category of cards in Series I is the Original 9. This is the most challenging subset in the series, and each card has been designed to illustrate just how special the Original 9 cards are. The front of each card shows one of the Original 9 Beanie Babies introduced by Ty in 1994, along with the Beanie's name, style number, and Official Club logo.

The cards themselves are as original as the Beanies they represent — printed on clear mylar, they look unlike any other card in the series. The front of each card is foil stamped with "Original 9" in one of four colors: red, blue, silver, and gold, with gold being the most difficult variation to find. Each card in the Original 9 category is crash-numbered 1 of a limited amount, making them very rare indeed!

The back of each card gives birth dates, issue dates, and retirement dates, along with the Beanie Baby's poem and the series number, all printed on an opaque white background. The Original 9 cards are numbered 1 to 9, and the odds of finding one are 1 in 117 packs!

Card #
1

*C*hocolate•4015

R B S G

Date Purchased: _____

Price Paid: _____

Market Value: _____

Purchased At: _____

4015
Original 9

CHOCOLATE
THE MOOSE

GOLD
Difficult
SILVER
BLUE
RED
Moderate

CHOCOLATE
the Moose
BEANIE BABIES®
OFFICIAL CLUB®
Birthday: 4-27-93
Issued: 1-8-94

1

Licorice, gum and
peppermint candy
This moose always has
these handy
There is one
more thing
he likes to eat
Can you guess his
favorite sweet?

Card #
2

*C*ubbie•4010

4010
Original 9

CUBBIE
THE BROWN BEAR

GOLD
Difficult
SILVER
BLUE
RED
Moderate

CUBBIE
the Brown Bear
BEANIE BABIES®
OFFICIAL CLUB®
Birthday: 11-14-93
Issued: 1-8-94
Retired:
12-31-97

2

Cubbie used to eat
crackers and honey
And what happened
to him was funny
He was stung by
fourteen bees
Now Cubbie eats
broccoli and cheese.

R B S G

Date Purchased: _____

Price Paid: _____

Market Value: _____

Purchased At: _____

ORIGINAL 9 CARDS

89

1st Edition

Flash • 4021

Card # **3**

	R	B	S	G
Date Purchased:				
Price Paid:				
Market Value:				
Purchased At:				

4021
Original 9

FLASH
THE DOLPHIN

FLASH
the Dolphin
BEANIE BABIES®
OFFICIAL CLUB®
Birthday: 5-13-93
Issued: 1-8-94
Retired:
5-11-97

3

You know dolphins
are a smart breed
Our friend Flash knows how
to read
Splash the whale is the one who taught her
Although reading is difficult
under the water!

GOLD — Difficult
SILVER
BLUE
RED
— Moderate

Legs • 4020

Card # **4**

GOLD — Difficult
SILVER
BLUE
RED
— Moderate

4020
Original 9

LEGS
THE FROG

LEGS
the Frog
BEANIE BABIES®
OFFICIAL CLUB®
Birthday: 4-25-93
Issued: 1-8-94
Retired:
10-1-97

Legs lives in
a hollow log
Legs likes to play leap frog
If you like to hang out
at the lake
Legs will be the
new friend
you'll make!

4

	R	B	S	G
Date Purchased:				
Price Paid:				
Market Value:				
Purchased At:				

ORIGINAL 9 CARDS

Card #
5

Patti • 4025

	R	B	S	G
Date Purchased:				
Price Paid:				
Market Value:				
Purchased At:				

4025

THE MAROON PLATYPUS

PATTI
the Maroon Platypus
BEANIE BABIES®
OFFICIAL CLUB®
Birthday: 1-6-93
Issued: 2-28-95
Retired:
12-31-97

Ran into Patti one
day while walking
Believe me she wouldn't
stop talking
Listened and listened
to her speak
That would explain her
extra large beak!

5

GOLD Difficult
SILVER
BLUE
RED

Moderate

Card #
6

Pinchers • 4026

4026

THE LOBSTER

GOLD Difficult
SILVER
BLUE
RED

Moderate

PINCHERS
the Lobster
BEANIE BABIES®
OFFICIAL CLUB®
Birthday: 6-19-93
Issued: 1-8-94
Retired:
5-1-98

This lobster loves
to pinch
Eating his food
inch by inch
Balancing carefully with his tail
Moving forward slow as
a snail!

6

	R	B	S	G
Date Purchased:				
Price Paid:				
Market Value:				
Purchased At:				

ORIGINAL 9 CARDS

ORIGINAL 9 CARDS

Splash · 4022

Card #
7

	R	B	S	G
Date Purchased:				
Price Paid:				
Market Value:				
Purchased At:				

4022
Original
9

SPLASH
THE WHALE

SPLASH
the Whale
BEANIE BABIES®
OFFICIAL CLUB®
Birthday: 7-8-93
Issued: 1-8-94
Retired:
5-11-97

7

Splash loves to jump and dive
He's the fastest whale alive
He always wins the 100 yard dash
With a victory jump he'll make
a splash!

GOLD — Difficult
SILVER
BLUE
RED
— Moderate

Spot · 4000

Card #
8

GOLD — Difficult
SILVER
BLUE
RED
— Moderate

4000
Original
9

SPOT THE DOG
WITHOUT A SPOT

SPOT
the Dog
BEANIE BABIES®
OFFICIAL CLUB®
Birthday: 1-3-93
Issued: 1-8-94
Retired:
4-13-94

8

See Spot sprint,
see Spot run
You and Spot will have
lots of fun
Watch out now
because he's not slow
Just stand back
and watch him go!

SPOT THE DOG

	R	B	S	G
Date Purchased:				
Price Paid:				
Market Value:				
Purchased At:				

Card #
9

*S*quealer · 4005

R   B   S   G

Date Purchased: ___ ___ ___ ___

Price Paid: ___ ___ ___ ___

Market Value: ___ ___ ___ ___

Purchased At: _____

GOLD — Difficult

SILVER
BLUE
RED

— Moderate

4005
Original 9

SQUEALER
THE PIG

9

Squealer likes to
joke around
He is known as
class clown
Listen to his stories
for awhile
There is no doubt
he'll make you smile!

SQUEALER
the Pig
BEANIE BABIES®
OFFICIAL CLUB®
Birthday: 4-23-93
Issued: 1-8-94
Retired:
5-1-98

ORIGINAL 9 CARDS

PUZZLE CARDS

Puzzle Cards

Each pack of Series I Beanie Babies Collector's Cards contains one of eight different Puzzle cards. Each of these cards is a full-color, two-sided mini-jigsaw puzzle. Puzzle cards are purely for fun and give Beanie fans a chance to see some of their favorites in different indoor and outdoor scenes. Puzzle cards have titles, including: Born to be Wild, It's a Dog's Life, Star Spangled Beanies, the Faces of Teddy, the Original 9, the Tropical Heat Wave, and Winter Beanie Wonderland.

There is an eighth untitled puzzle that depicts a tropical scene on one side, and Beanie Babies dogs on the other. (Ty Warner's own dog, Cleo, is pictured hanging with the rest of the pack in this puzzle, and the tropical scene on the flip side is actually one of Ty's favorite vacation spots!)

Star Spangled Beanies

Date Purchased: _____

Purchased At: _____

Born to be Wild

Date Purchased: _____

Purchased At: _____

PUZZLE CARDS

95

PUZZLE CARDS

The Faces of Teddy

Date Purchased: _____

Purchased At: _____

It's a Dog's Life

Date Purchased: _____

Purchased At: _____

The Original Nine

Date Purchased: _____

Purchased At: _____

Tropical Heat Wave

Date Purchased: _____

Purchased At: _____

PUZZLE CARDS

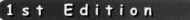

Winter Beanie Wonderland

Date Purchased: _____

Purchased At: _____

Ty's Picks

Date Purchased: _____

Purchased At: _____

PUZZLE CARDS

The Common Cards

The same quality standards found in Series I Common cards can be found in Series II. The Series II Common cards each represent a Beanie not shown in Series II and round out the representation of every Beanie produced by Ty up until the time the Series II cards were printed.

Series II Common cards are a continuation of Series I. The same attention to quality and design detail is used with this series. Also, as with Series I, some Common cards are easier to find than others.

On the back of each Common card you'll find birthday and issue dates, along with the series number, little-known facts about the animal or character that Beanie represents, and their poem. There are 100 Common cards numbered 150 to 249 in Series II. These cards are easy to moderately difficult to find.

COMMON CARDS

1st Edition

COMMON CARDS

1997 Holiday Teddy · 4200

Card # 150

HOLIDAY TEDDY 1997

BEANIE BABIES
Series II
4200
1999

Date Purchased: _____

Price Paid: _____

Purchased At: _____

Market Value: _____

BEANIE BABIES OFFICIAL CLUB™
HOLIDAY TEDDY
1997
Birthday: 12-25-96
Issued: 10-1-97
Beanie Babies are
special no doubt
All filled with love—
inside and out
Wishes for fun times
filled with joy
Ty's holiday teddy
is a magic toy!
150

LITTLE-KNOWN FACTS:
On Christmas Day 1939,
the Charles Dickens clas-
sic A Christmas Carol was
read over the radio for
the first time by Lionel
Barrymore. The reading
of this story has become
an annual holiday event.

4200   ©1999 TY INC. BEANIE BABIES OFFICIAL CLUB

Moderate
Easy

1998 Holiday Teddy · 4204

Card # 151

Moderate
Easy

HOLIDAY TEDDY 1998

BEANIE BABIES
Series II
4204
1999

BEANIE BABIES OFFICIAL CLUB™
HOLIDAY TEDDY
1998
Birthday: 12-25-98
Issued: 9-30-98
Dressed in his pj's and
ready for bed
Hugs given,
goodnights said
This little beanie will
stay close at night
Ready for a hug at first
morning light!
151

LITTLE-KNOWN FACTS:
1997 was the first year
that Ty produced a Holiday
Teddy commemorating the
holiday season. That tra-
dition was maintained in
1998 with this special
Holiday Teddy. We hope
the tradition continues!

4204   ©1999 TY INC. BEANIE BABIES OFFICIAL CLUB

Date Purchased: _____

Price Paid: _____

Purchased At: _____

Market Value: _____

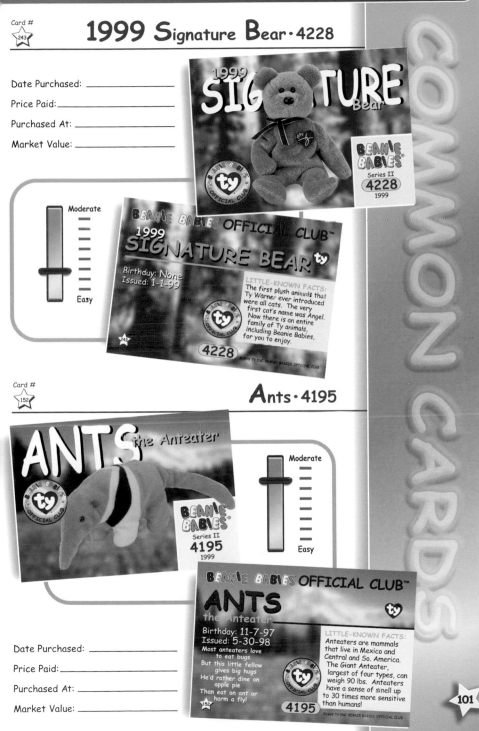

COMMON CARDS

Card #
243

1999 Signature Bear • 4228

Date Purchased: _____

Price Paid: _____

Purchased At: _____

Market Value: _____

Moderate

Easy

BEANIE BABIES OFFICIAL CLUB

1999
SIGNATURE BEAR ty

Birthday: None
Issued: 1-1-99

LITTLE-KNOWN FACTS:
The first plush animals that Ty Warner ever introduced were all cats. The very first cat's name was Angel. Now there is an entire family of Ty animals, including Beanie Babies, for you to enjoy.

4228

©1999 TY INC BEANIE BABIES OFFICIAL CLUB

Card #
152

Ants • 4195

ANTS the Anteater

Series II
4195
1999

Moderate

Easy

BEANIE BABIES OFFICIAL CLUB

ANTS
the Anteater

Birthday: 11-7-97
Issued: 5-30-98

Most anteaters love
to eat bugs
But this little fellow
gives big hugs
He'd rather dine on
apple pie
Than eat an ant or
harm a fly!

LITTLE-KNOWN FACTS:
Anteaters are mammals that live in Mexico and Central and So. America. The Giant Anteater, largest of four types, can weigh 90 lbs. Anteaters have a sense of smell up to 30 times more sensitive than humans!

4195

©1999 TY INC BEANIE BABIES OFFICIAL CLUB

Date Purchased: _____

Price Paid: _____

Purchased At: _____

Market Value: _____

101

COMMON CARDS

Batty • 4035

Card # 153

BATTY the Bat

BEANIE BABIES OFFICIAL CLUB
Series II
4035
1999

Date Purchased: _____

Price Paid: _____

Purchased At: _____

Market Value: _____

BEANIE BABIES OFFICIAL CLUB™
BATTY
the Bat
Birthday: 10-29-96
Issued: 10-1-97

Bats may make
some people jitter
Please don't be scared
of this critter
If you're lonely
or have nothing to do
This Beanie Babie
would love to hug you!
153

LITTLE-KNOWN FACTS:
Bats are the only mammals
capable of sustained flight.
They can be found all over
the world, except in the
Arctic Zone and certain
remote islands. Contrary
to popular belief, bats,
while they do have poor
eyesight, are not blind.
4035
©1999 TY INC. BEANIE BABIES OFFICIAL CLUB

Moderate
Easy

Bessie • 4009

Card # 154

Moderate
Easy

BESSIE the Cow

BEANIE BABIES
Series II
4009
1999

BEANIE BABIES OFFICIAL CLUB™
BESSIE
the Cow
Birthday: 6-27-95
Issued: 6-3-95
Bessie the Cow likes
to dance and sing
Because music is her
favorite thing
Every night when you
are counting sheep
She'll sing you a song
to help you sleep!
154

LITTLE-KNOWN FACTS:
There are approximately
10 million cows in the U.S.
Most dairy cows (cattle)
produce about 15,000 lbs
of milk and 550 lbs of
butterfat. The major
breeds are the Holstein-
Friesian, Brown Swiss,
Ayrshire, and Jersey.
4009
©1999 TY INC. BEANIE BABIES OFFICIAL CLUB

Date Purchased: _____

Price Paid: _____

Purchased At: _____

Market Value: _____

Card #
155

Bongo • 4067

Date Purchased: _____

Price Paid: _____

Purchased At: _____

Market Value: _____

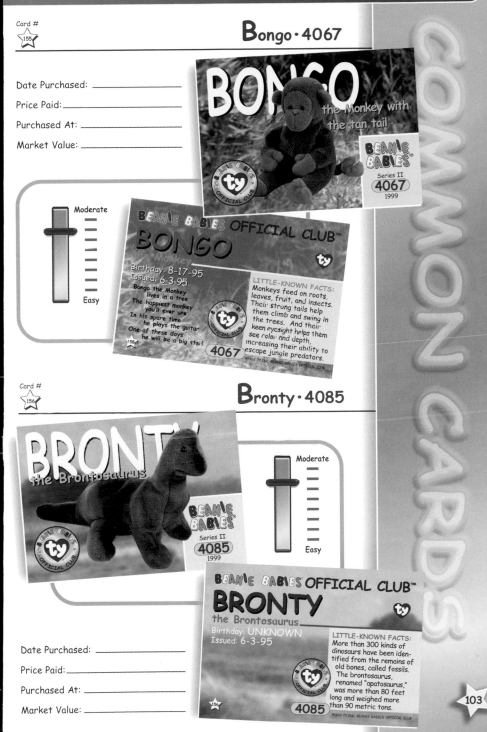

Moderate

Easy

BONGO the Monkey with the tan tail

BEANIE BABIES
Series II
4067
1999

BEANIE BABIES OFFICIAL CLUB™
BONGO
ty

Birthday: 8-17-95
Issued: 6-3-95
Bongo the Monkey
lives in a tree
The happiest monkey
you'll ever see
In his spare time
he plays the guitar
One of these days
he will be a big star!

4067

LITTLE-KNOWN FACTS:
Monkeys feed on roots,
leaves, fruit, and insects.
Their strong tails help
them climb and swing in
the trees. And their
keen eyesight helps them
see color and depth,
increasing their ability to
escape jungle predators.
©1999 TY INC. BEANIE BABIES OFFICIAL CLUB

Card #
156

Bronty • 4085

BRONTY the Brontosaurus

BEANIE BABIES
Series II
4085
1999

Moderate

Easy

BEANIE BABIES OFFICIAL CLUB™
BRONTY
ty
the Brontosaurus
Birthday: UNKNOWN
Issued: 6-3-95

LITTLE-KNOWN FACTS:
More than 300 kinds of
dinosaurs have been iden-
tified from the remains of
old bones, called fossils.
The brontosaurus,
renamed "apatosaurus,"
was more than 80 feet
long and weighed more
than 90 metric tons.

4085
©1999 TY INC. BEANIE BABIES OFFICIAL CLUB

Date Purchased: _____

Price Paid: _____

Purchased At: _____

Market Value: _____

COMMON CARDS

Bubbles • 4078

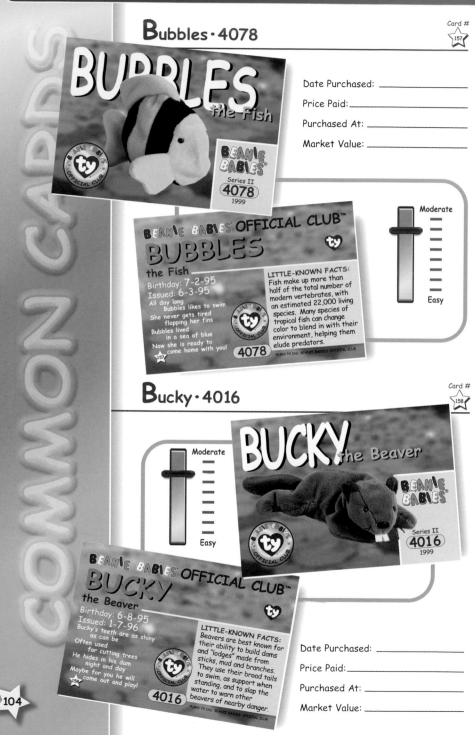

Date Purchased: _____

Price Paid: _____

Purchased At: _____

Market Value: _____

BEANIE BABIES OFFICIAL CLUB™

BUBBLES
the Fish
Birthday: 7-2-95
Issued: 6-3-95
All day long
    Bubbles likes to swim
She never gets tired
    flapping her fins
Bubbles lived
    in a sea of blue
Now she is ready to
    come home with you!

LITTLE-KNOWN FACTS:
Fish make up more than
half of the total number of
modern vertebrates, with
an estimated 22,000 living
species. Many species of
tropical fish can change
color to blend in with their
environment, helping them
elude predators.

4078
©1999 TY INC. BEANIE BABIES. OFFICIAL CLUB

Moderate — Easy

Bucky • 4016

Moderate — Easy

BEANIE BABIES OFFICIAL CLUB™

BUCKY
the Beaver
Birthday: 6-8-95
Issued: 1-7-96
Bucky's teeth are as shiny
    as can be
Often used
    for cutting trees
He hides in his dam
    night and day
Maybe for you he will
    come out and play!

LITTLE-KNOWN FACTS:
Beavers are best known for
their ability to build dams
and "lodges" made from
sticks, mud and branches.
They use their broad tails
to swim, as support when
standing, and to slap the
water to warn other
beavers of nearby danger.

4016
©1999 TY INC. BEANIE BABIES OFFICIAL CLUB

Date Purchased: _____

Price Paid: _____

Purchased At: _____

Market Value: _____

Card #
159

Butch • 4227

Date Purchased: _____

Price Paid: _____

Purchased At: _____

Market Value: _____

Moderate

Easy

BEANIE BABIES OFFICIAL CLUB™

BUTCH
the Bull Terrier
Birthday: 10-2-98
Issued: 1-1-99

Going to the pet shop
to buy dog food
I ran into Butch
in a good mood
"Come to the pet shop
down the street!"
"Be a good dog,
I'll buy you a treat!"

LITTLE-KNOWN FACTS:
Bull terriers are a loyal
breed of dog originally
raised in England in the
1800's. They have short
hair and are of stout
build, often weighing
40-60 lbs.

4227

Card #
160

Canyon • 4212

Moderate

Easy

BEANIE BABIES OFFICIAL CLUB™

CANYON
the Cougar
Birthday: 5-29-98
Issued: 9-30-98

Canyon the Cougar
lives in the mountains
He does not like subways
or city hall fountains
He's a sure-footed feline
who just loves to play
So Canyon should always
be one hug away.

LITTLE-KNOWN FACTS:
The cougar, also known as
a puma or mountain lion,
has made a dramatic
resurgence from near
extinction. Inhabiting
mountainous regions from
Canada to So. America,
cougars use rocky terrain
as camouflage.

4212

Date Purchased: _____

Price Paid: _____

Purchased At: _____

Market Value: _____

105

COMMON CARDS

Chilly • 4012

Card #
161

CHILLY the Polar Bear

Series II
4012
1999

Date Purchased: _____

Price Paid: _____

Purchased At: _____

Market Value: _____

BEANIE BABIES OFFICIAL CLUB™

CHILLY
the Polar Bear

Birthday: UNKNOWN
Issued: 6-25-94

LITTLE-KNOWN FACTS:
Polar bears live in the snowy Arctic and throughout the North Polar basin. The long hair between a polar bear's feet helps keep its feet warm and provides improved traction when crossing icy terrain.

161
4012
©1999 TY INC. BEANIE BABIES OFFICIAL CLUB

Moderate

Easy

Chocolate • 4015

Card #
162

Moderate

Easy

CHOCOLATE the Moose

Series II
4015
1999

BEANIE BABIES OFFICIAL CLUB™

CHOCOLATE
the Moose

Birthday: 4-27-93
Issued: 1-8-94

Licorice, gum,
and peppermint candy
This moose always
has these handy
There is one more thing
he likes to eat
Can you guess
his favorite sweet?

LITTLE-KNOWN FACTS:
The largest member of the deer family, moose can stand almost 8 feet tall and can weigh up to 1,800 lbs. Some moose antlers can reach 5 feet across! They like to eat aquatic vegetation and are excellent swimmers.

162
4015
©1999 TY INC. BEANIE BABIES OFFICIAL CLUB

Date Purchased: _____

Price Paid: _____

Purchased At: _____

Market Value: _____

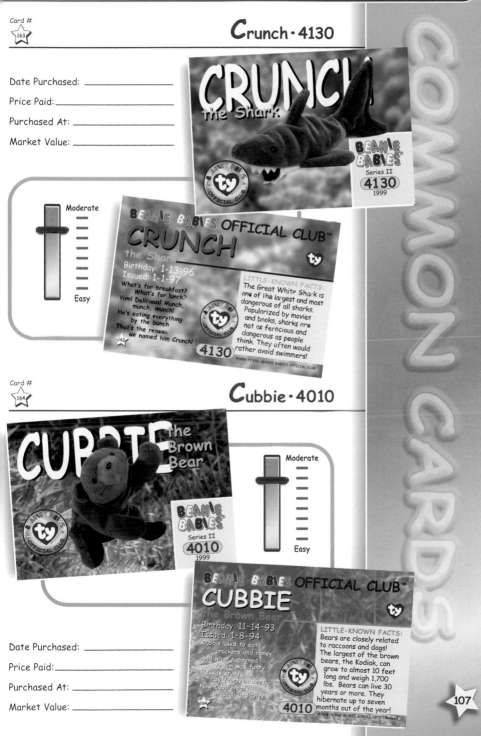

Card #
163

Crunch • 4130

Date Purchased: _____

Price Paid: _____

Purchased At: _____

Market Value: _____

Moderate

Easy

BEANIE BABIES OFFICIAL CLUB

CRUNCH
the Shark

Birthday: 1-13-96
Issued: 1-1-97

What's for breakfast?
What's for lunch?
Yum! Delicious! Munch,
munch, munch!
He's eating everything
by the bunch
That's the reason
we named him Crunch!

163

LITTLE-KNOWN FACTS:
The Great White Shark is one of the largest and most dangerous of all sharks. Popularized by movies and books, sharks are not as ferocious and dangerous as people think. They often would rather avoid swimmers!

4130
©1999 TY INC. BEANIE BABIES OFFICIAL CLUB

CRUNCH
the Shark

BEANIE BABIES
Series II
4130
1999

Card #
164

Cubbie • 4010

CUBBIE
the Brown Bear

BEANIE BABIES
Series II
4010
1999

Moderate

Easy

BEANIE BABIES OFFICIAL CLUB

CUBBIE
the Brown Bear

Birthday: 11-14-93
Issued: 1-8-94

Cubbie used to eat
crackers and honey
And what happened
to him was funny
He was stung
by fourteen bees
Now Cubbie eats
broccoli and cheese!

164

LITTLE-KNOWN FACTS:
Bears are closely related to raccoons and dogs! The largest of the brown bears, the Kodiak, can grow to almost 10 feet long and weigh 1,700 lbs. Bears can live 30 years or more. They hibernate up to seven months out of the year!

4010
©1999 TY INC. BEANIE BABIES OFFICIAL CLUB

Date Purchased: _____

Price Paid: _____

Purchased At: _____

Market Value: _____

COMMON CARDS

107

1st Edition

COMMON CARDS

Derby • 4008

DERBY the Horse with fur mane and tail

BEANIE BABIES OFFICIAL CLUB

Series II
4008
1999

Date Purchased: _____

Price Paid: _____

Purchased At: _____

Market Value: _____

BEANIE BABIES® OFFICIAL CLUB™

DERBY
the Horse
Birthday: 9-16-95
Issued: 1-1-99

All the other horses
used to tattle
Because Derby never
wore his saddle
He left the stables,
and the horses too
Just so Derby
can be with you!

LITTLE-KNOWN FACTS:
The horse is a close relative
of the African zebra and
the donkey. Horses have
helped humans with work
and travel ever since
ancient Babylonia! We
can thank the Spanish for
bringing horses to America
in the 16th century.

165

4008

©1999 TY INC. BEANIE BABIES OFFICIAL CLUB

Moderate

Easy

Derby • 4008

Moderate

Easy

DERBY the Horse

BEANIE BABIES

Series II
4008
1999

BEANIE BABIES® OFFICIAL CLUB™

DERBY
the Horse
Birthday: 9-16-95
Issued: 6-3-95

All the other horses
used to tattle
Because Derby never
wore his saddle
He left the stables,
and the horses too
Just so Derby
can be with you!

LITTLE-KNOWN FACTS:
Horses have 44 teeth. Six
incisors help cut grass and
other roughage. Fourteen
molars help grind and
chew. This healthy diet
lets horses adapt and
survive different envi-
ronments and ecosystems
all over the world!

166

4008

©1999 TY INC. BEANIE BABIES OFFICIAL CLUB

Date Purchased: _____

Price Paid: _____

Purchased At: _____

Market Value: _____

COMMON CARDS

Card #
167

Digger • 4027

Date Purchased: _____

Price Paid: _____

Purchased At: _____

Market Value: _____

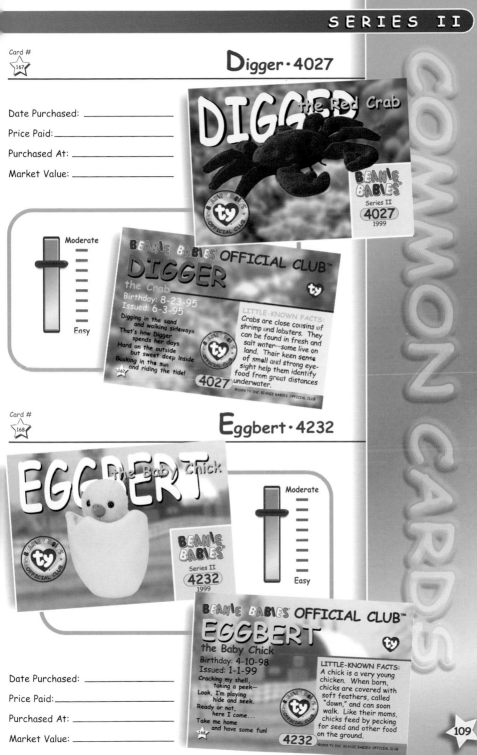

DIGGER the Red Crab

BEANIE BABIES
Series II
4027
1999

Moderate

Easy

BEANIE BABIES OFFICIAL CLUB™
DIGGER
the Crab
Birthday: 8-23-95
Issued: 6-3-95
Digging in the sand
and walking sideways
That's how Digger
spends her days
Hard on the outside
but sweet deep inside
Basking in the sun
and riding the tide!
167
4027

LITTLE-KNOWN FACTS:
Crabs are close cousins of
shrimp and lobsters. They
can be found in fresh and
salt water—some live on
land. Their keen sense
of small and strong eye-
sight help them identify
food from great distances
underwater.
©1999 TY INC. BEANIE BABIES OFFICIAL CLUB

Card #
168

Eggbert • 4232

EGGBERT the Baby Chick

BEANIE BABIES
Series II
4232
1999

Moderate

Easy

BEANIE BABIES OFFICIAL CLUB™
EGGBERT
the Baby Chick
Birthday: 4-10-98
Issued: 1-1-99
Cracking my shell,
taking a peek—
Look, I'm playing
hide and seek.
Ready or not,
here I come...
Take me home
and have some fun!
168
4232

LITTLE-KNOWN FACTS:
A chick is a very young
chicken. When born,
chicks are covered with
soft feathers, called
"down," and can soon
walk. Like their moms,
chicks feed by pecking
for seed and other food
on the ground.
©1999 TY INC. BEANIE BABIES OFFICIAL CLUB

Date Purchased: _____

Price Paid: _____

Purchased At: _____

Market Value: _____

COMMON CARDS

Ewey • 4219

Card # 169

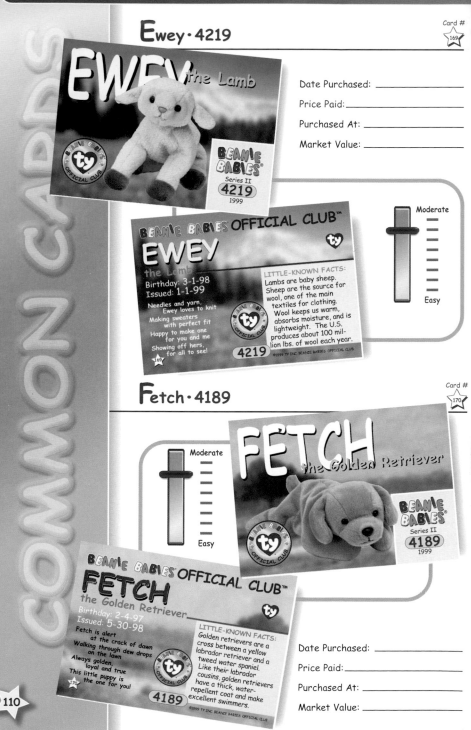

EWEY the Lamb

BEANIE BABIES
Series II
4219
1999

Date Purchased: _____

Price Paid: _____

Purchased At: _____

Market Value: _____

BEANIE BABIES OFFICIAL CLUB™

EWEY
the Lamb
Birthday: 3-1-98
Issued: 1-1-99

Needles and yarn,
Ewey loves to knit
Making sweaters
with perfect fit
Happy to make one
for you and me
Showing off hers,
for all to see!

4219

LITTLE-KNOWN FACTS:
Lambs are baby sheep.
Sheep are the source for
wool, one of the main
textiles for clothing.
Wool keeps us warm,
absorbs moisture, and is
lightweight. The U.S.
produces about 100 mil-
lion lbs. of wool each year.
©1999 TY INC. BEANIE BABIES OFFICIAL CLUB

Moderate

Easy

Fetch • 4189

Card # 170

Moderate

Easy

FETCH
the Golden Retriever

BEANIE BABIES
Series II
4189
1999

BEANIE BABIES OFFICIAL CLUB™

FETCH
the Golden Retriever
Birthday: 2-4-97
Issued: 5-30-98

Fetch is alert
at the crack of dawn
Walking through dew drops
on the lawn
Always golden,
loyal and true
This little puppy is
the one for you!

4189

LITTLE-KNOWN FACTS:
Golden retrievers are a
cross between a yellow
labrador retriever and a
tweed water spaniel.
Like their labrador
cousins, golden retrievers
have a thick, water-
repellent coat and make
excellent swimmers.
©1999 TY INC. BEANIE BABIES OFFICIAL CLUB

Date Purchased: _____

Price Paid: _____

Purchased At: _____

Market Value: _____

Card #
171

Flash·4021

Date Purchased: _____

Price Paid: _____

Purchased At: _____

Market Value: _____

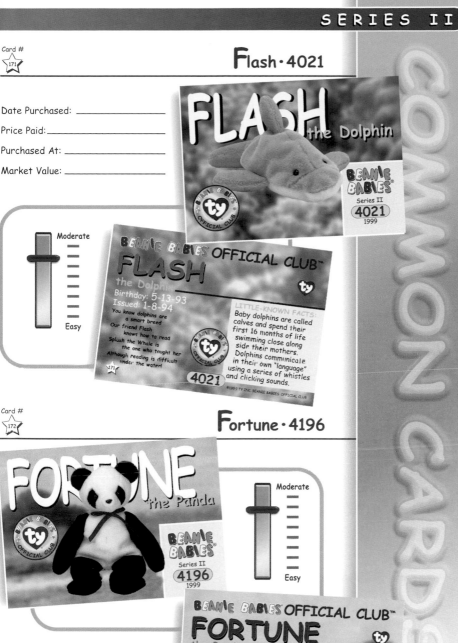

Moderate

Easy

Card #
172

Fortune·4196

Moderate

Easy

Date Purchased: _____

Price Paid: _____

Purchased At: _____

Market Value: _____

COMMON CARDS

111

1st Edition

Fuzz · 4237

FUZZ the Bear

BEANIE BABIES® Series II
4237
1999

BEANIE BABIES OFFICIAL CLUB™

FUZZ the Bear

Birthday: 7-23-98
Issued: 1-1-99

Look closely at
this handsome bear
His texture is
really quite rare.
With golden highlights
in his hair
He has class,
style and flair!

173

LITTLE-KNOWN FACTS:
North American brown
bears include the grizzly
and the kodiak. The
kodiak is the largest
bear, standing 9 feet
high and weighing more
than 1500 lbs!

4237   ©1999 TY INC. BEANIE BABIES OFFICIAL CLUB

Moderate — Easy

Date Purchased: _____

Price Paid: _____

Purchased At: _____

Market Value: _____

Germania · 4236

Moderate — Easy

GERMANIA the Bear

BEANIE BABIES® Series II
4236
1999

BEANIE BABIES OFFICIAL CLUB™

GERMANIA the Bear

Birthday: 10-3-90
Issued: 1-1-99

Einigkeit und Recht
und Freiheit
ist der Deutschen
Einheislied,
Allen Kindern brav
un fein
Soll dieser Bär
das liebste sein!

174

LITTLE-KNOWN FACTS:
Germania is an exclusive
Beanie Baby, distributed
only in Germany!
Germany is a country in
Europe, located just
south of France and
England—next to
Austria.

4236   ©1999 TY INC. BEANIE BABIES OFFICIAL CLUB

Date Purchased: _____

Price Paid: _____

Purchased At: _____

Market Value: _____

Card #
★ 177

Goatee • 4235

Date Purchased: _____

Price Paid: _____

Purchased At: _____

Market Value: _____

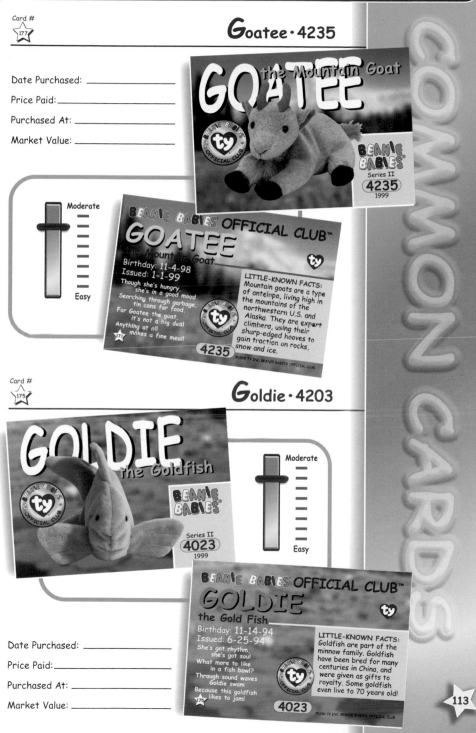

Moderate — Easy

Card #
★ 175

Goldie • 4203

Date Purchased: _____

Price Paid: _____

Purchased At: _____

Market Value: _____

113

COMMON CARDS

1st Edition

Goochy • 4230

GOOCHY
the Jellyfish

BEANIE BABIES®
Series II
4230
1999

Date Purchased: _____

Price Paid: _____

Purchased At: _____

Market Value: _____

BEANIE BABIES OFFICIAL CLUB™

GOOCHY
the Jellyfish
Birthday: 11-18-98
Issued: 1-1-99

Swirl, swish, squirm
and wiggle
Listen closely, hear
him giggle
The most ticklish jellyfish
you'll ever meet
Even though he has
no feet!

LITTLE-KNOWN FACTS:
Jellyfish are made up of
99% water! The most
common form of jellyfish,
the medusa, swims by
contracting the muscles
around its body. The
largest jellyfish can
measures more than six
feet wide!

4230 ©1999 TY INC BEANIE BABIES OFFICIAL CLUB

Moderate

Easy

Happy • 4061

Moderate

Easy

HAPPY
the Lavender
Hippo

BEANIE BABIES®
Series II
4061
1999

BEANIE BABIES OFFICIAL CLUB™

HAPPY
the Hippo
Birthday: 2-25-94
Issued: 6-3-95

Happy the Hippo
loves to wade
In the river
and in the shade
When Happy shoots water
out of his snout
You know he's happy
without a doubt!

LITTLE-KNOWN FACTS:
A hippopotamus has a
thick protective skin,
which is covered with a
sticky pink fluid. This
pink substance helps to
protect the hippo from
sunburn as well as from
excessive water loss
through the skin.

4061 ©1999 TY INC BEANIE BABIES OFFICIAL CLUB

Date Purchased: _____

Price Paid: _____

Purchased At: _____

Market Value: _____

Card #
179

Hippie · 4218

Date Purchased: _____

Price Paid: _____

Purchased At: _____

Market Value: _____

Moderate

Easy

BEANIE BABIES OFFICIAL CLUB™

HIPPIE
the Ty-Dye Bunny

Birthday: 5-4-98
Issued: 1-1-99

Hippie fell into the dye,
they say
While coloring eggs,
one spring day
From the tips of his ears,
down to his toes
Colors of springtime,
he proudly shows!

LITTLE-KNOWN FACTS:
The term "hippie" became
popular in the 1960's and
70's and was applied pri-
marily to youth who
were "hip" to popular
trends. Like this bunny,
hippies were hip to
peace, love and ty-dye!

4218
©1999 TY INC BEANIE BABIES OFFICIAL CLUB

Card #
180

Hippity · 4119

Moderate

Easy

Date Purchased: _____

Price Paid: _____

Purchased At: _____

Market Value: _____

BEANIE BABIES OFFICIAL CLUB™

HIPPITY
the Mint Bunny

Birthday: 6-1-96
Issued: 1-1-97

Hippity is a cute
little bunny
Dressed in green,
he looks quite funny
Twitching his nose
in the air
Sniffing a flower
here and there!

LITTLE-KNOWN FACTS:
The Easter Bunny visits
each year on Easter,
bringing joy and happiness
to little children every-
where. The Easter
Bunny's specially painted
eggs can be found all over
the world on Easter!

4119
©1999 TY INC BEANIE BABIES OFFICIAL CLUB

COMMON CARDS

115

1st Edition

Hope · 4213

HOPE
the Praying Bear

BEANIE BABIES
Series II
4213
1999

Date Purchased: _____

Price Paid: _____

Purchased At: _____

Market Value: _____

BEANIE BABIES OFFICIAL CLUB™
HOPE
the Praying Bear

Birthday: 3-23-98
Issued: 1-1-99

Every night when
it's time for bed
Fold your hands
and bow your head
An angelic face,
a heart that's true
You have a friend
to pray with you!

LITTLE-KNOWN FACTS:
Praying for world peace
can bring us all new hope.
And wishing that love
and happiness come to
all the world's children
is a great way to start
changing the world for
the better!

181   4213   ©1999 TY INC. BEANIE BABIES OFFICIAL CLUB

Moderate

Easy

Hoppity · 4117

Moderate

Easy

HOPPITY
the Rose Bunny

BEANIE BABIES
Series II
4117
1999

BEANIE BABIES OFFICIAL CLUB™
HOPPITY
the Rose Bunny

Birthday: 4-3-96
Issued: 1-1-97

Hopscotch is what
she likes to play
If you don't join in,
she'll hop away
So play a game if
you have the time,
She likes to play,
rain or shine!

LITTLE-KNOWN FACTS:
Rabbits and hares are
closely related, but you
can see differences if
you know when to look.
When baby rabbits are
first born, their eyes
are closed—while baby
hares are born with
their eyes wide open!

182   4117   ©1999 TY INC. BEANIE BABIES OFFICIAL CLUB

Date Purchased: _____

Price Paid: _____

Purchased At: _____

Market Value: _____

COMMON CARDS

Card #
183

Humphrey · 4060

Date Purchased: _____

Price Paid: _____

Purchased At: _____

Market Value: _____

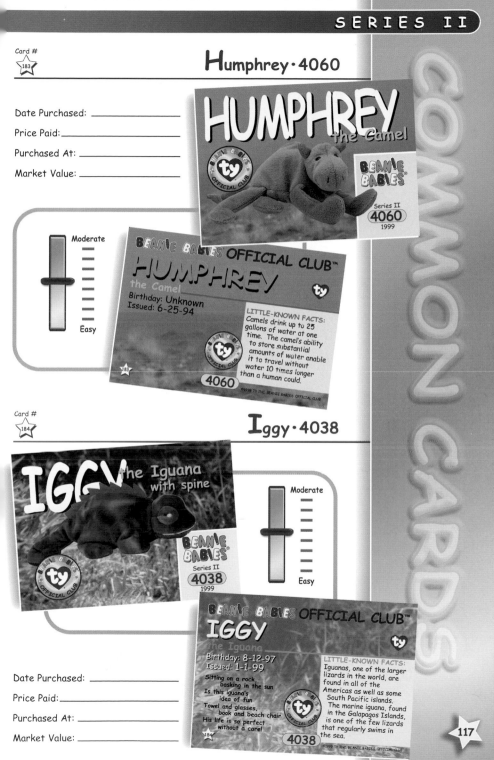

Moderate

Easy

BEANIE BABIES OFFICIAL CLUB™
HUMPHREY
the Camel
Birthday: Unknown
Issued: 6-25-94

LITTLE-KNOWN FACTS:
Camels drink up to 25 gallons of water at one time. The camel's ability to store substantial amounts of water enable it to travel without water 10 times longer than a human could.

4060

Card #
184

Iggy · 4038

IGGY the Iguana with spine

BEANIE BABIES
Series II
4038
1999

Moderate

Easy

BEANIE BABIES OFFICIAL CLUB™
IGGY
the Iguana
Birthday: 8-12-97
Issued: 1-1-99

Sitting on a rock, basking in the sun
Is this iguana's idea of fun
Towel and glasses, book and beach chair
His life is so perfect without a care!

LITTLE-KNOWN FACTS:
Iguanas, one of the larger lizards in the world, are found in all of the Americas as well as some South Pacific islands. The marine iguana, found in the Galapagos Islands, is one of the few lizards that regularly swims in the sea.

4038
©1999 TY INC. BEANIE BABIES OFFICIAL CLUB

Date Purchased: _____

Price Paid: _____

Purchased At: _____

Market Value: _____

117

1st Edition

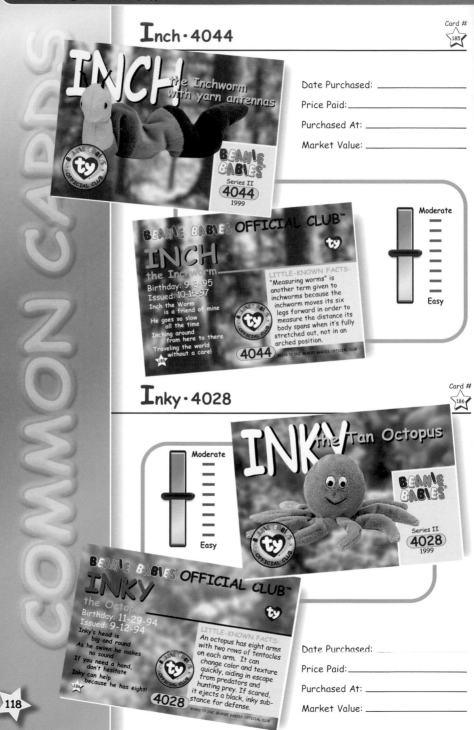

Inch • 4044

Card #
185

INCH the Inchworm with yarn antennas

Series II
4044
1999

Date Purchased: _____

Price Paid: _____

Purchased At: _____

Market Value: _____

BEANIE BABIES OFFICIAL CLUB™

INCH
the Inchworm
Birthday: 9-3-95
Issued: 10-15-97
Inch the Worm
  is a friend of mine
He goes so slow
  all the time
Inching around
  from here to there
Traveling the world
  without a care!
185
4044

LITTLE-KNOWN FACTS:
"Measuring worms" is another term given to inchworms because the inchworm moves its six legs forward in order to measure the distance its body spans when it's fully stretched out, not in an arched position.

©1999 TY INC. BEANIE BABIES OFFICIAL CLUB

Moderate

Easy

Inky • 4028

Card #
186

Moderate

Easy

INKY the Tan Octopus

BEANIE BABIES

Series II
4028
1999

BEANIE BABIES OFFICIAL CLUB™

INKY
the Octopus
Birthday: 11-29-94
Issued: 9-12-94
Inky's head is
  big and round
As he swims he makes
  no sound
If you need a hand,
  don't hesitate
Inky can help
  because he has eight!
186
4028

LITTLE-KNOWN FACTS:
An octopus has eight arms with two rows of tentacles on each arm. It can change color and texture quickly, aiding in escape from predators and hunting prey. If scared, it ejects a black, inky substance for defense.

©1993 TY INC. BEANIE BABIES OFFICIAL CLUB

Date Purchased: _____

Price Paid: _____

Purchased At: _____

Market Value: _____

COMMON CARDS

118

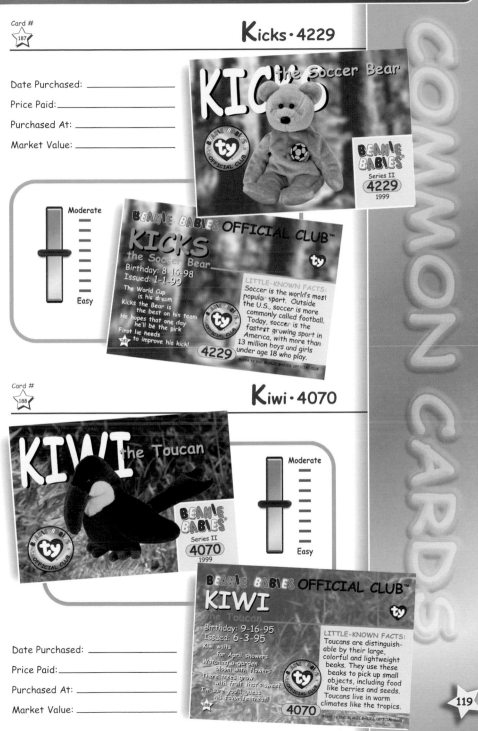

Card #
187

Kicks · 4229

Date Purchased: _____

Price Paid: _____

Purchased At: _____

Market Value: _____

Moderate

Easy

Card #
188

Kiwi · 4070

Date Purchased: _____

Price Paid: _____

Purchased At: _____

Market Value: _____

COMMON CARDS

119

1st Edition

Lefty • 4086

Card #
189

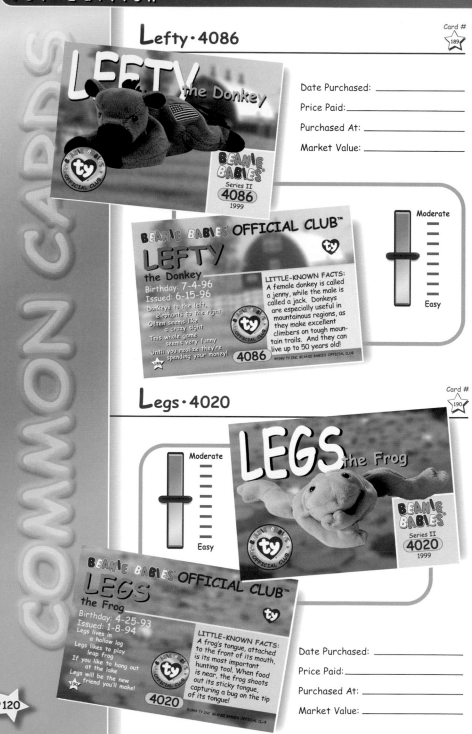

LEFTY the Donkey

BEANIE BABIES
Series II
4086
1999

Date Purchased: _____

Price Paid: _____

Purchased At: _____

Market Value: _____

BEANIE BABIES OFFICIAL CLUB™
LEFTY
the Donkey
Birthday: 7-4-96
Issued: 6-15-96
Donkeys to the left,
   elephants to the right!
Often seems like
   a crazy sight
This whole game
   seems very funny
Until you realize they're
   spending your money!

189

LITTLE-KNOWN FACTS:
A female donkey is called
a jenny, while the male is
called a jack. Donkeys
are especially useful in
mountainous regions, as
they make excellent
climbers on tough moun-
tain trails. And they can
live up to 50 years old!

4086
©1999 TY INC. BEANIE BABIES OFFICIAL CLUB

Moderate

Easy

Legs • 4020

Card #
190

Moderate

Easy

LEGS the Frog

BEANIE BABIES
Series II
4020
1999

BEANIE BABIES OFFICIAL CLUB™
LEGS
the Frog
Birthday: 4-25-93
Issued: 1-8-94
Legs lives in
   a hollow log
Legs likes to play
   leap frog
If you like to hang out
   at the lake
Legs will be the new
   friend you'll make!

189

LITTLE-KNOWN FACTS:
A frog's tongue, attached
to the front of its mouth,
is its most important
hunting tool. When food
is near, the frog shoots
out its sticky tongue,
capturing a bug on the tip
of its tongue!

4020
©1999 TY INC. BEANIE BABIES OFFICIAL CLUB

Date Purchased: _____

Price Paid: _____

Purchased At: _____

Market Value: _____

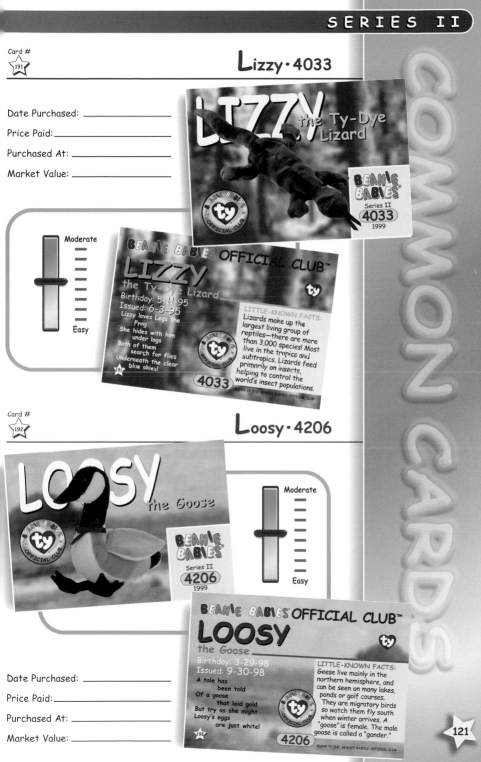

Card #
191

Lizzy • 4033

Date Purchased: _____

Price Paid: _____

Purchased At: _____

Market Value: _____

Moderate

Easy

LIZZY
the Ty-Dye Lizard

BEANIE BABIES
Series II
4033
1999

BEANIE BABIES OFFICIAL CLUB™
LIZZY
the Ty-Dye Lizard
Birthday: 5-11-95
Issued: 6-3-95
Lizzy loves Legs the
Frog
She hides with him
under logs
Both of them
search for flies
Underneath the clear
blue skies!

LITTLE-KNOWN FACTS:
Lizards make up the
largest living group of
reptiles—there are more
than 3,000 species! Most
live in the tropics and
subtropics. Lizards feed
primarily on insects,
helping to control the
world's insect populations.

4033
©1999 TY INC. BEANIE BABIES OFFICIAL CLUB

Card #
192

Loosy • 4206

LOOSY
the Goose

BEANIE BABIES
Series II
4206
1999

Moderate

Easy

BEANIE BABIES OFFICIAL CLUB™
LOOSY
the Goose
Birthday: 3-29-98
Issued: 9-30-98
A tale has
been told
Of a goose
that laid gold
But try as she might
Loosy's eggs
are just white!

LITTLE-KNOWN FACTS:
Geese live mainly in the
northern hemisphere, and
can be seen on many lakes,
ponds or golf courses.
They are migratory birds
so watch them fly south
when winter arrives. A
"goose" is female. The male
goose is called a "gander."

4206
©1999 TY INC. BEANIE BABIES OFFICIAL CLUB

Date Purchased: _____

Price Paid: _____

Purchased At: _____

Market Value: _____

1st Edition

COMMON CARDS

Luke · 4214

Date Purchased: _____

Price Paid: _____

Purchased At: _____

Market Value: _____

Moderate

Easy

LUKE
the Black Labrador

Birthday: 6-15-98
Issued: 1-1-99

After chewing on
your favorite shoes
Luke gets tired,
takes a snooze.
Who wouldn't love
a puppy like this?
Give him a hug,
he'll give you a kiss!

LITTLE-KNOWN FACTS:
There are three types of
labradors: black, yellow
and chocolate. The breed
was first introduced in
Newfoundland, Canada,
and later as a separate
breed in 1903. Labs, as
they are often called,
are excellent swimmers!

Mac · 4225

Moderate

Easy

MAC
the Cardinal

Birthday: 6-10-98
Issued: 1-1-99

Mac tries hard
to prove he's the best
Swinging his bat harder
than the rest
Breaking records,
enjoying the game
Hitting home runs
is his claim to fame!

LITTLE-KNOWN FACTS:
In 1998, Mark McGwire
of the St. Louis Cardinals
set a major league base-
ball record with 70
home runs in a season.
This famous game
ended in a 6-3 victory
over the Montreal Expos.

Date Purchased: _____

Price Paid: _____

Purchased At: _____

Market Value: _____

Card #
196

Mel • 4162

Date Purchased: _____

Price Paid: _____

Purchased At: _____

Market Value: _____

Moderate

Easy

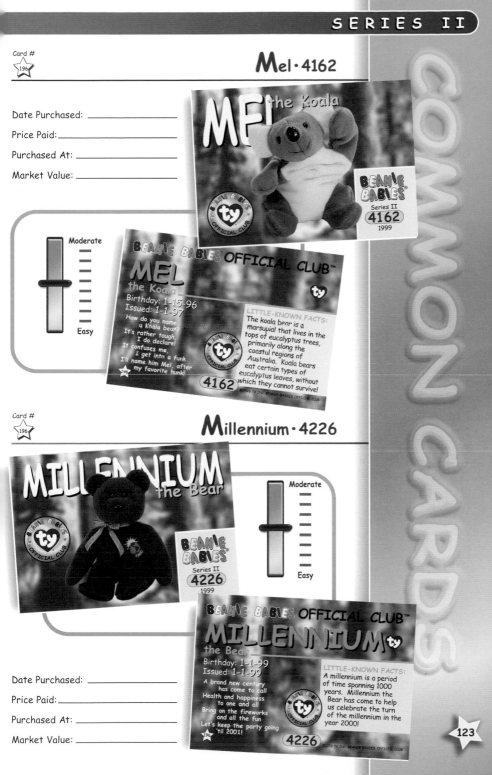

BEANIE BABIES OFFICIAL CLUB™

MEL
the Koala
Birthday: 1-15-96
Issued: 1-1-97
How do you name
a Koala bear?
It's rather tough,
I do declare!
It confuses me,
I get into a funk
I'll name him Mel, after
my favorite hunk!

LITTLE-KNOWN FACTS:
The koala bear is a
marsupial that lives in the
tops of eucalyptus trees,
primarily along the
coastal regions of
Australia. Koala bears
eat certain types of
eucalyptus leaves, without
which they cannot survive!

4162

MEL the Koala

BEANIE BABIES
Series II
4162
1999

Card #
196

Millennium • 4226

MILLENNIUM
the Bear

BEANIE BABIES
Series II
4226
1999

Moderate

Easy

BEANIE BABIES OFFICIAL CLUB™

MILLENNIUM
the Bear
Birthday: 1-1-99
Issued: 1-1-99
A brand new century
has come to call
Health and happiness
to one and all
Bring on the fireworks
and all the fun
Let's keep the party going
'til 2001!

LITTLE-KNOWN FACTS:
A millennium is a period
of time spanning 1000
years. Millennium the
Bear has come to help
us celebrate the turn
of the millennium in the
year 2000!

4226

Date Purchased: _____

Price Paid: _____

Purchased At: _____

Market Value: _____

COMMON CARDS

123

COMMON CARDS

Mooch • 4224

Card # 197

Date Purchased: _____

Price Paid: _____

Market Value: _____

Purchased At: _____

BEANIE BABIES OFFICIAL CLUB™

MOOCH
the Spider Monkey
Birthday: 8-1-98
Issued: 1-1-99
Look in the treetops,
up towards the sky
Swinging from branches
way up high
Tempt him with
a banana or fruit
When he's hungry,
he acts so cute!

LITTLE-KNOWN FACTS:
Spider Monkeys live in
Central and South America.
They have long, thin tails
and great acrobatic
ability. Using these
tails like a third hand,
they grab branches and
swing from tree to tree
throughout the jungle.

4224

Moderate — Easy

Mystic • 4007

Card # 198

Moderate — Easy

BEANIE BABIES OFFICIAL CLUB™

MYSTIC
the Unicorn
Birthday: 5-21-94
Issued: 1-1-99
Once upon a time
so far away
A unicorn was born
one day in May
Keep Mystic with you,
she's a prize
You'll see the magic
in her blue eyes!

LITTLE-KNOWN FACTS:
The unicorn is often
found in late medieval
religious paintings.
Usually portrayed as
pure white, unicorns
have been thought of
as a symbol of purity.

4007

Date Purchased: _____

Price Paid: _____

Market Value: _____

Purchased At: _____

COMMON CARDS

Card #
199

Mystic • 4007

Date Purchased: _____

Price Paid: _____

Market Value: _____

Purchased At: _____

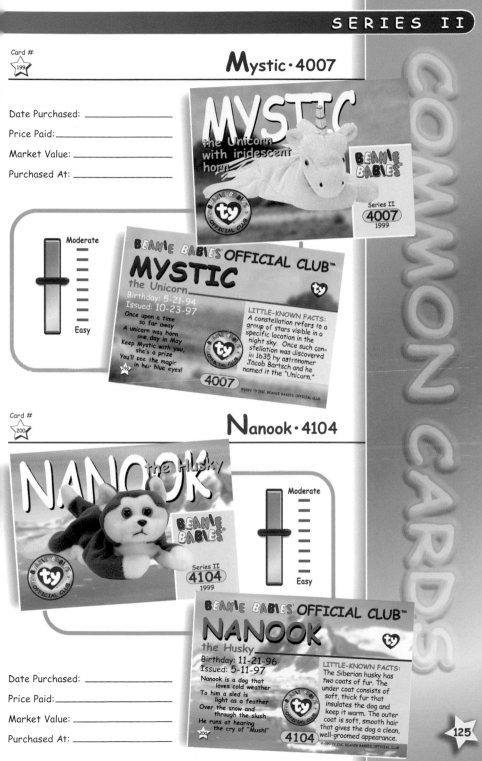

MYSTIC
the Unicorn
with iridescent
horn

BEANIE BABIES

Series II
4007
1999

Moderate

Easy

BEANIE BABIES OFFICIAL CLUB™
MYSTIC
the Unicorn
Birthday: 5-21-94
Issued: 10-23-97

Once upon a time
so far away
A unicorn was born
one day in May
Keep Mystic with you,
she's a prize
You'll see the magic
in her blue eyes!

LITTLE-KNOWN FACTS:
A constellation refers to a
group of stars visible in a
specific location in the
night sky. Once such con-
stellation was discovered
in 1635 by astronomer
Jacob Bartsch and he
named it the "Unicorn."

4007
©1999 TY INC. BEANIE BABIES OFFICIAL CLUB

Card #
200

Nanook • 4104

NANOOK
the Husky

BEANIE BABIES

Series II
4104
1999

Moderate

Easy

BEANIE BABIES OFFICIAL CLUB™
NANOOK
the Husky
Birthday: 11-21-96
Issued: 5-11-97

Nanook is a dog that
loves cold weather
To him a sled is
light as a feather
Over the snow and
through the slush
He runs at hearing
the cry of "Mush!"

LITTLE-KNOWN FACTS:
The Siberian husky has
two coats of fur. The
under coat consists of
soft, thick fur that
insulates the dog and
keep it warm. The outer
coat is soft, smooth hair
that gives the dog a clean,
well-groomed appearance.

4104
©1999 TY INC. BEANIE BABIES OFFICIAL CLUB

Date Purchased: _____

Price Paid: _____

Market Value: _____

Purchased At: _____

125

1st Edition

Nibbler · 4216

Date Purchased: _____

Price Paid: _____

Market Value: _____

Purchased At: _____

Moderate

Easy

BEANIE BABIES OFFICIAL CLUB™

NIBBLER
the Rabbit

Birthday: 4-6-98
Issued: 1-1-99

Twitching her nose,
she looks so sweet
Small in size,
she's very petite
Soft and furry,
hopping with grace
She'll visit your garden,
her favorite place!

201

LITTLE-KNOWN FACTS:
In the wild, rabbits
spend much of their time
hopping around wooded
and open areas. As
pets, the more room
rabbits have to play in,
the more delightful
they are as companions.

4216

©1999 TY INC. BEANIE BABIES OFFICIAL CLUB

Nibbly · 4217

Moderate

Easy

BEANIE BABIES OFFICIAL CLUB™

NIBBLY
the Brown Rabbit

Birthday: 5-7-98
Issued: 1-1-99

Wonderful ways
to spend a day
Bright and sunny
in the month of May
Hopping around
as trees sway
Looking for friends,
out to play!

202

LITTLE-KNOWN FACTS:
Rabbits and hares have
large front teeth, short
tails, and hind legs and feet
adapted for running and
jumping. Hares refer to
larger, hopping animals
with long ears and legs,
whose young are born with
their eyes wide open.

4217

©1999 TY INC. BEANIE BABIES OFFICIAL CLUB

Date Purchased: _____

Price Paid: _____

Market Value: _____

Purchased At: _____

Card #
203

Nip·4003

Date Purchased: _____

Price Paid: _____

Market Value: _____

Purchased At: _____

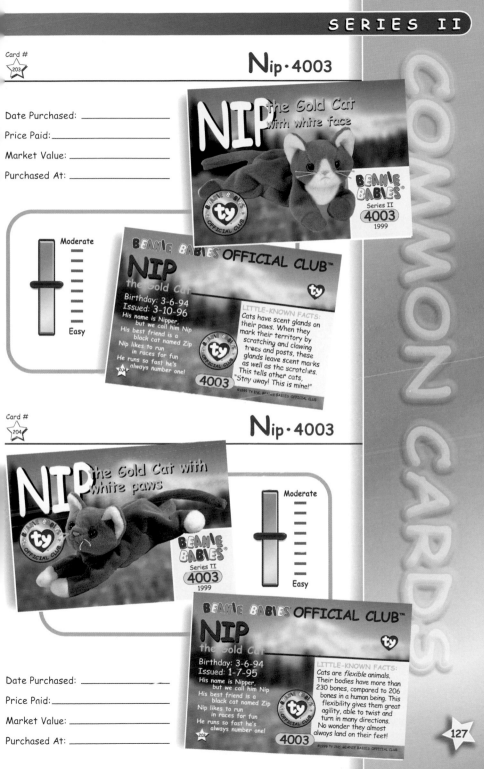

Moderate

Easy

NIP
the Gold Cat with white face

BEANIE BABIES
Series II
4003
1999

BEANIE BABIES OFFICIAL CLUB™

NIP
the Gold Cat

Birthday: 3-6-94
Issued: 3-10-96
His name is Nipper,
but we call him Nip
His best friend is a
black cat named Zip
Nip likes to run
in races for fun
He runs so fast he's
always number one!

LITTLE-KNOWN FACTS:
Cats have scent glands on
their paws. When they
mark their territory by
scratching and clawing
trees and posts, these
glands leave scent marks
as well as the scratches.
This tells other cats,
"Stay away! This is mine!"

4003
©1999 TY INC. BEANIE BABIES OFFICIAL CLUB

Card #
204

Nip·4003

NIP
the Gold Cat with
white paws

BEANIE BABIES
Series II
4003
1999

Moderate

Easy

BEANIE BABIES OFFICIAL CLUB™

NIP
the Gold Cat

Birthday: 3-6-94
Issued: 1-7-95
His name is Nipper,
but we call him Nip
His best friend is a
black cat named Zip
Nip likes to run
in races for fun
He runs so fast he's
always number one!

LITTLE-KNOWN FACTS:
Cats are flexible animals.
Their bodies have more than
230 bones, compared to 206
bones in a human being. This
flexibility gives them great
agility, able to twist and
turn in many directions.
No wonder they almost
always land on their feet!

4003
©1999 TY INC. BEANIE BABIES OFFICIAL CLUB

Date Purchased: _____

Price Paid: _____

Market Value: _____

Purchased At: _____

COMMON CARDS

127

1st Edition

Patti · 4025

Card #
205

PATTI the Maroon Platypus

BEANIE BABIES
Series II
4025
1999

Date Purchased: _____
Price Paid: _____
Market Value: _____
Purchased At: _____

BEANIE BABIES OFFICIAL CLUB™

PATTI
the Maroon Platypus

Birthday: 1-6-93
Issued: 1-8-94

Ran into Patti
one day while walking
Believe me she
wouldn't stop talking
Listened and listened
to her speak
That would explain
her extra large beak!

4025

LITTLE-KNOWN FACTS:
The duckbill platypus
has webbed front feet
and a sleek body, which
makes them very strong
swimmers. Platypus
always live near the
water, primarily streams
and rivers in regions of
Tasmania and Australia.

©1999 TY INC. BEANIE BABIES OFFICIAL CLUB

Moderate

Easy

Peanut · 4062

Card #
206

PEANUT the Elephant

BEANIE BABIES
Series II
4062
1999

Moderate

Easy

BEANIE BABIES OFFICIAL CLUB™

PEANUT
the Elephant

Birthday: 1-25-95
Issued: 6-3-95

Peanut the elephant
walks on tip-toes
Quietly sneaking
wherever she goes
She'll sneak up on you
and a hug you will get
Peanut's a friend
you won't soon forget!

4062

LITTLE-KNOWN FACTS:
The elephant can eat up
to 500 lbs of food a day!
No wonder it's the largest
living land mammal. Its
trunk, an elongated
upper lip and nose, lifts
heavy objects, carries
items, and transfers food
and water to its mouth.

©1999 TY INC. BEANIE BABIES OFFICIAL CLUB

Date Purchased: _____
Price Paid: _____
Market Value: _____
Purchased At: _____

COMMON CARDS

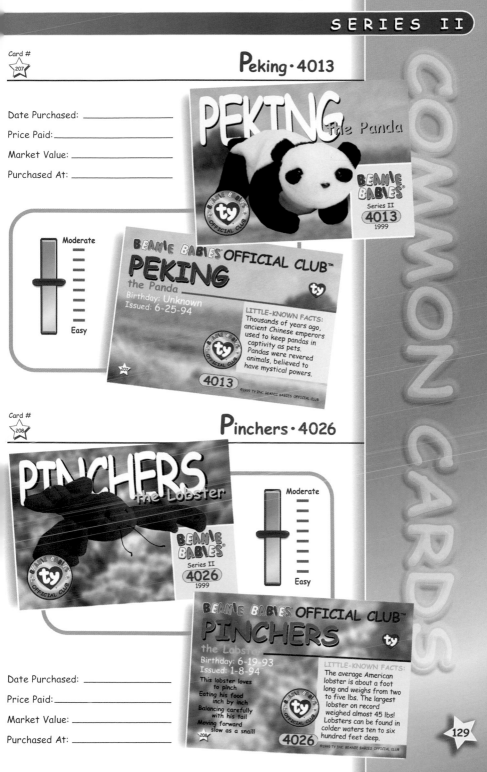

Card #
☆ 207

Peking • 4013

Date Purchased: _____

Price Paid: _____

Market Value: _____

Purchased At: _____

Moderate
Easy

PEKING
the Panda
Birthday: Unknown
Issued: 6-25-94

LITTLE-KNOWN FACTS:
Thousands of years ago,
ancient Chinese emperors
used to keep pandas in
captivity as pets.
Pandas were revered
animals, believed to
have mystical powers.

4013
©1999 TY INC. BEANIE BABIES OFFICIAL CLUB

Card #
☆ 208

Pinchers • 4026

PINCHERS
the Lobster

Series II
4026
1999

Moderate
Easy

PINCHERS
the Lobster
Birthday: 6-19-93
Issued: 1-8-94

This lobster loves
to pinch
Eating his food
inch by inch
Balancing carefully
with his tail
Moving forward
slow as a snail!

LITTLE-KNOWN FACTS:
The average American
lobster is about a foot
long and weighs from two
to five lbs. The largest
lobster on record
weighed almost 45 lbs!
Lobsters can be found in
colder waters ten to six
hundred feet deep.

4026
©1999 TY INC. BEANIE BABIES OFFICIAL CLUB

Date Purchased: _____

Price Paid: _____

Market Value: _____

Purchased At: _____

COMMON CARDS

129

Card #
211

Quackers • 4024

Date Purchased: _____

Price Paid: _____

Market Value: _____

Purchased At: _____

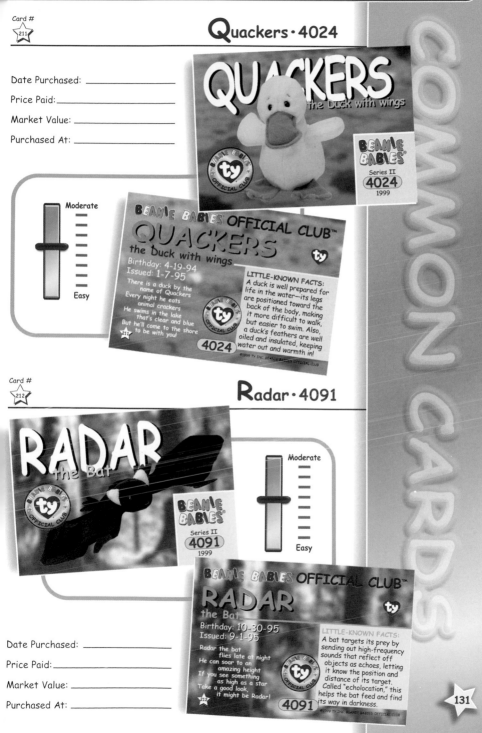

Moderate — Easy

Card #
212

Radar • 4091

Moderate — Easy

Date Purchased: _____

Price Paid: _____

Market Value: _____

Purchased At: _____

COMMON CARDS

1st Edition

Rainbow • 4037

Card #
213

Date Purchased: _____

Price Paid: _____

Market Value: _____

Purchased At: _____

RAINBOW
the Chameleon
with hood & tongue

BEANIE BABIES®
Series II
4037
1999

BEANIE BABIES OFFICIAL CLUB™
RAINBOW
the Chameleon

Birthday: 10-14-97
Issued: 1-1-99

Red, green, blue and yellow
This chameleon is
a colorful fellow.
A blend of colors,
his own unique hue
Rainbow was made
especially for you!

213

4037

LITTLE-KNOWN FACTS:
Chameleons change color
due to fear, temperature
change, and changes in
light intensity. They also
have large eyes that
move independently,
making it easy for them
to spot danger coming
from any direction.

©1999 TY INC. BEANIE BABIES OFFICIAL CLUB

Moderate

Easy

Roam • 4209

Card #
214

Moderate

Easy

ROAM
the Buffalo

BEANIE BABIES
Series II
4209
1999

BEANIE BABIES OFFICIAL CLUB™
ROAM
the Buffalo

Birthday: 9-27-98
Issued: 9-30-98

Once roaming wild
on the American land
Tall and strong,
woolly and grand
So rare and special
is this guy
Find him quickly,
he's quite a buy!

4209

LITTLE-KNOWN FACTS:
The American buffalo, or
"bison," weighs up to 2,500
lbs and can run 40 miles
per hour. At one time
almost 60 million buffalo
roamed throughout
North America. Today,
living in protected areas,
only 30,000 bison remain.

©1999 TY INC. BEANIE BABIES OFFICIAL CLUB

Date Purchased: _____

Price Paid: _____

Market Value: _____

Purchased At: _____

COMMON CARDS

Card #
215

Sammy • 4215

Date Purchased: _____

Price Paid: _____

Market Value: _____

Purchased At: _____

Moderate

Easy

BEANIE BABIES OFFICIAL CLUB™

SAMMY
the Ty-Dye Bear

Birthday: 6-23-98
Issued: 1-1-99

As Sammy steps up
to the plate
The crowd gets excited,
can hardly wait
We know Sammy
won't let us down
He makes us the happiest
fans in town!

4215

LITTLE-KNOWN FACTS:
Sammy Sosa was the 1998
National Baseball League's
most valuable player. Along
with Mark McGwire, Sosa
broke the long-standing
home run record, formerly
held by Roger Maris, of 61
home runs in a season.

© 1999 TY INC BEANIE BABIES OFFICIAL CLUB

SAMMY
the Ty-Dye Bear

BEANIE BABIES®
Series II
4215
1999

Card #
216

Santa • 4203

SANTA
the Santa

BEANIE BABIES®
Series II
4203
1999

Moderate

Easy

BEANIE BABIES OFFICIAL CLUB™

SANTA
the Santa

Birthday: 12-6-98
Issued: 9-30-98

Known by all
in his suit of red
Piles of presents
on his sled
Generous and giving,
he brings us joy
Peace and love,
plus this special toy!

216

4203

LITTLE-KNOWN FACTS:
Santa Claus has many
names around the world.
He's also known as Saint
Nicholas, Saint Nick, Kris
Kringle, and Father
Christmas. Don't forget
to leave cookies and milk
for Santa on Christmas
Eve—it can be a long night!

© 1999 TY INC BEANIE BABIES OFFICIAL CLUB

Date Purchased: _____

Price Paid: _____

Market Value: _____

Purchased At: _____

COMMON CARDS

133

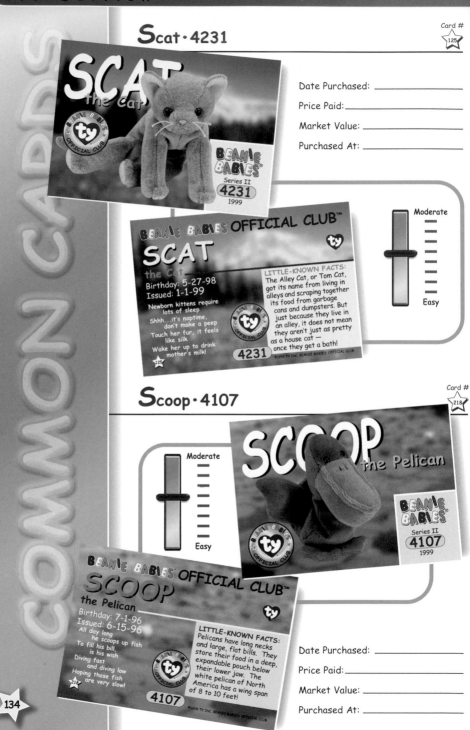

1st Edition

Scat · 4231

Card #
125

SCAT
the cat

BEANIE BABIES
Series II
4231
1999

Date Purchased: _____

Price Paid: _____

Market Value: _____

Purchased At: _____

BEANIE BABIES OFFICIAL CLUB™

SCAT
the Cat

Birthday: 5-27-98
Issued: 1-1-99

Newborn kittens require
lots of sleep
Shhh... it's naptime,
   don't make a peep
Touch her fur, it feels
   like silk
Wake her up to drink
   mother's milk!

LITTLE-KNOWN FACTS:
The Alley Cat, or Tom Cat,
got its name from living in
alleys and scraping together
its food from garbage
cans and dumpsters. But
just because they live in
an alley, it does not mean
they aren't just as pretty
as a house cat —
once they get a bath!

4231

©1999 TY INC. BEANIE BABIES OFFICIAL CLUB

Moderate
Easy

Scoop · 4107

Card #
218

Moderate
Easy

SCOOP
the Pelican

BEANIE BABIES
Series II
4107
1999

BEANIE BABIES OFFICIAL CLUB™

SCOOP
the Pelican

Birthday: 7-1-96
Issued: 6-15-96

All day long
   he scoops up fish
To fill his bill,
   is his wish
Diving fast
   and diving low
Hoping those fish
   are very slow!

LITTLE-KNOWN FACTS:
Pelicans have long necks
and large, flat bills. They
store their food in a deep,
expandable pouch below
their lower jaw. The
white pelican of North
America has a wing span
of 8 to 10 feet!

4107

©1999 TY INC. BEANIE BABIES OFFICIAL CLUB

Date Purchased: _____

Price Paid: _____

Market Value: _____

Purchased At: _____

COMMON CARDS

Card #
219

Scorch · 4210

Date Purchased: _____

Price Paid: _____

Market Value: _____

Purchased At: _____

Moderate

Easy

SCORCH
the Dragon
Birthday: 7-31-98
Issued: 9-30-98

A magical mystery
with glowing wings
Made by wizards
and other things
Known to breathe fire
with lots of smoke
Scorch is really
a friendly ol' bloke!

LITTLE-KNOWN FACTS:
While many believe that
dragons are evil, some
civilizations believed
dragons were good and
shared the secrets of
the world with humans.
Vikings put carvings of
dragons their bouts to
help guide them.

4210

©1999 TY INC. BEANIE BABIES OFFICIAL CLUB

Card #
220

Slippery · 4222

Moderate

Easy

Slippery
the Seal
Birthday: 1-17-98
Issued: 1-1-99

In the ocean, near a
breaking wave
Slippery the seal acts
very brave
On his surfboard, he sees
a swell
He's riding the wave!
Oooops...he fell!

LITTLE-KNOWN FACTS:
Seals have streamlined
bodies, which make them
quick, agile swimmers.
Traveling in groups, they
often swim far from
their breeding grounds
to follow schools of
fish. And they almost
always get their catch!

4222

©1999 TY INC BEANIE BABIES OFFICIAL CLUB

Date Purchased: _____

Price Paid: _____

Market Value: _____

Purchased At: _____

135

COMMON CARDS

Slither · 4031

Card #
221

Date Purchased: _____

Price Paid: _____

Market Value: _____

Purchased At: _____

Sly · 4115

Card #
222

Date Purchased: _____

Price Paid: _____

Market Value: _____

Purchased At: _____

COMMON CARDS

Card #
223

Splash • 4022

Date Purchased: _____

Price Paid: _____

Market Value: _____

Purchased At: _____

Moderate

Easy

Card #
224

Spot • 4000

Date Purchased: _____

Price Paid: _____

Market Value: _____

Purchased At: _____

COMMON CARDS

137

COMMON CARDS

Spot • 4000

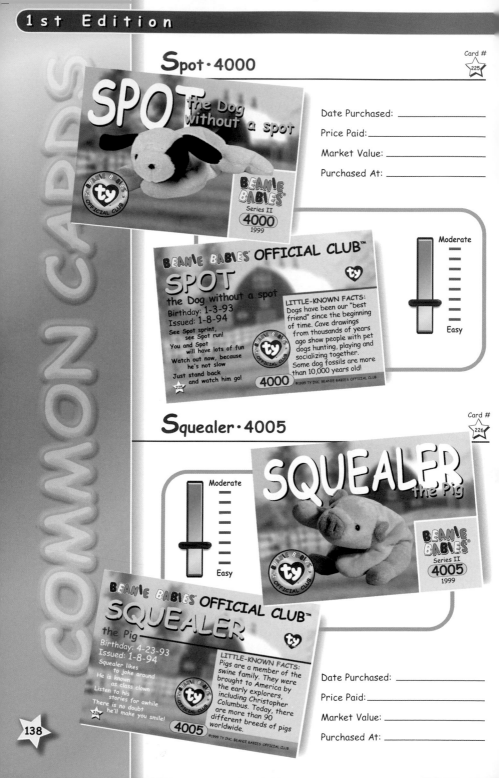

Card # 225

SPOT the Dog without a spot

BEANIE BABIES OFFICIAL CLUB
Series II
4000
1999

Date Purchased: _____

Price Paid: _____

Market Value: _____

Purchased At: _____

BEANIE BABIES OFFICIAL CLUB™

SPOT
the Dog without a spot
Birthday: 1-3-93
Issued: 1-8-94

See Spot sprint,
see Spot run!

You and Spot
will have lots of fun

Watch out now, because
he's not slow

Just stand back
and watch him go!

LITTLE-KNOWN FACTS:
Dogs have been our "best friend" since the beginning of time. Cave drawings from thousands of years ago show people with pet dogs hunting, playing and socializing together. Some dog fossils are more than 10,000 years old!

4000
©1999 TY INC. BEANIE BABIES OFFICIAL CLUB

Moderate

Easy

Squealer • 4005

Card # 226

Moderate

Easy

SQUEALER the Pig

BEANIE BABIES
Series II
4005
1999

BEANIE BABIES OFFICIAL CLUB™

SQUEALER
the Pig
Birthday: 4-23-93
Issued: 1-8-94

Squealer likes
to joke around

He is known
as class clown

Listen to his
stories for awhile

There is no doubt
he'll make you smile!

LITTLE-KNOWN FACTS:
Pigs are a member of the swine family. They were brought to America by the early explorers, including Christopher Columbus. Today, there are more than 90 different breeds of pigs worldwide.

4005
©1999 TY INC. BEANIE BABIES OFFICIAL CLUB

Date Purchased: _____

Price Paid: _____

Market Value: _____

Purchased At: _____

COMMON CARDS

Card #
227

Steg · 4087

Date Purchased: _____

Price Paid: _____

Market Value: _____

Purchased At: _____

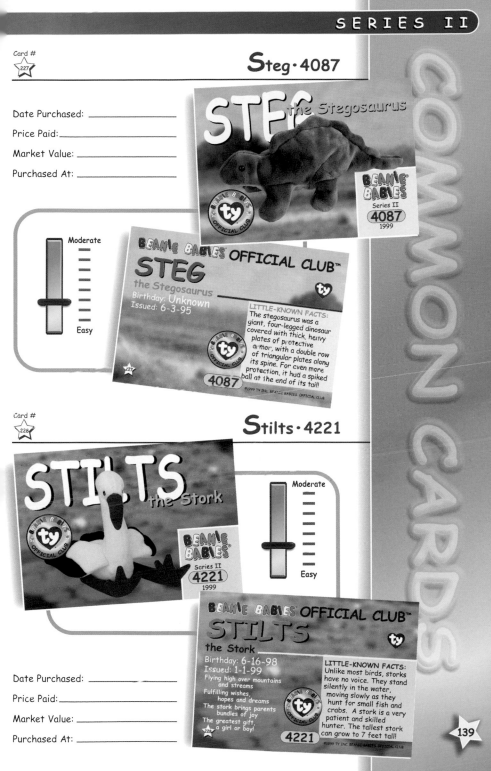

STEG the Stegosaurus

BEANIE BABIES
Series II
4087
1999

Moderate

Easy

BEANIE BABIES OFFICIAL CLUB™
STEG
the Stegosaurus
Birthday: Unknown
Issued: 6-3-95

LITTLE-KNOWN FACTS:
The stegosaurus was a giant, four-legged dinosaur covered with thick, heavy plates of protective armor, with a double row of triangular plates along its spine. For even more protection, it had a spiked ball at the end of its tail!

4087
©1999 TY INC. BEANIE BABIES OFFICIAL CLUB

Card #
228

Stilts · 4221

STILTS the Stork

BEANIE BABIES OFFICIAL CLUB

BEANIE BABIES
Series II
4221
1999

Moderate

Easy

BEANIE BABIES OFFICIAL CLUB™
STILTS
the Stork
Birthday: 6-16-98
Issued: 1-1-99
Flying high over mountains
and streams
Fulfilling wishes,
hopes and dreams
The stork brings parents
bundles of joy
The greatest gift,
a girl or boy!

LITTLE-KNOWN FACTS:
Unlike most birds, storks have no voice. They stand silently in the water, moving slowly as they hunt for small fish and crabs. A stork is a very patient and skilled hunter. The tallest stork can grow to 7 feet tall!

4221
©1999 TY INC. BEANIE BABIES OFFICIAL CLUB

Date Purchased: _____

Price Paid: _____

Market Value: _____

Purchased At: _____

139

COMMON CARDS

Stinger • 4193

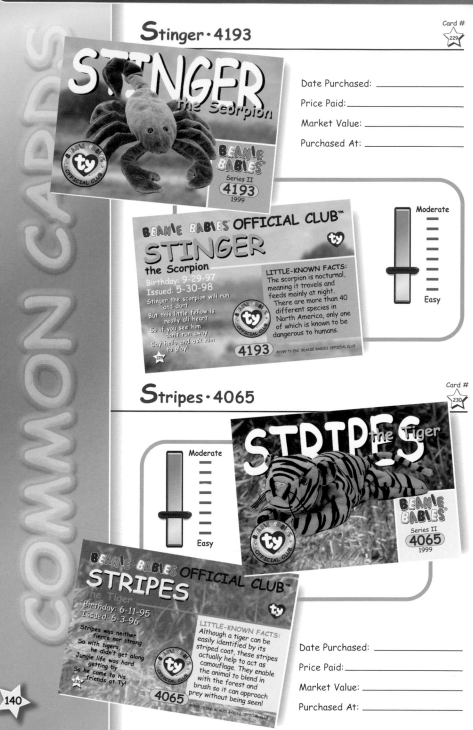

STINGER the Scorpion

BEANIE BABIES OFFICIAL CLUB
Series II
4193
1999

Date Purchased: _____

Price Paid: _____

Market Value: _____

Purchased At: _____

BEANIE BABIES OFFICIAL CLUB™
STINGER
the Scorpion
Birthday: 9-29-97
Issued: 5-30-98
Stinger the scorpion will run
and dart
But this little fellow is
really all heart
So if you see him
don't run away
Say hello and ask him
to play!
229

LITTLE-KNOWN FACTS:
The scorpion is nocturnal,
meaning it travels and
feeds mainly at night.
There are more than 40
different species in
North America, only one
of which is known to be
dangerous to humans.

4193   ©1999 TY INC BEANIE BABIES OFFICIAL CLUB

Moderate
Easy

Stripes • 4065

Moderate
Easy

STRIPES the Tiger

BEANIE BABIES
Series II
4065
1999

BEANIE BABIES OFFICIAL CLUB™
STRIPES
the Tiger
Birthday: 6-11-95
Issued: 6-3-96
Stripes was neither
fierce nor strong
So with tigers
he didn't get along
Jungle life was hard
getting by
So he came to his
friends at Ty!
230

LITTLE-KNOWN FACTS:
Although a tiger can be
easily identified by its
striped coat, these stripes
actually help to act as
camouflage. They enable
the animal to blend in
with the forest and
brush so it can approach
prey without being seen!

4065
©1999 TY INC. BEANIE BABIES OFFICIAL CLUB

Date Purchased: _____

Price Paid: _____

Market Value: _____

Purchased At: _____

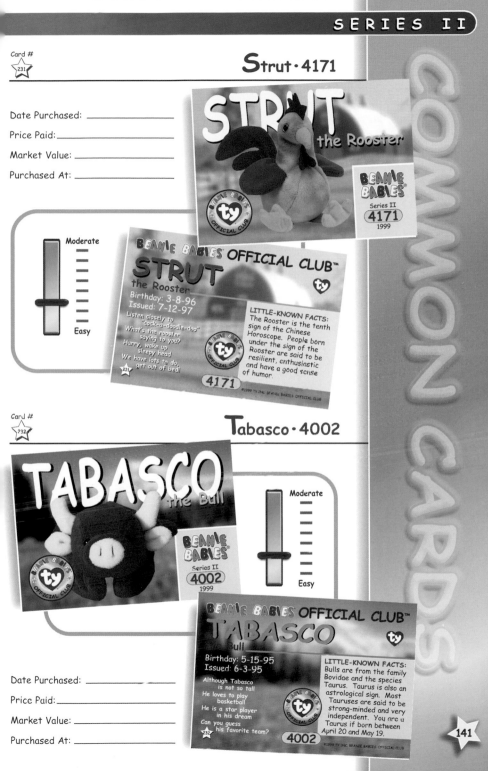

Card #
231

Strut • 4171

Date Purchased: _____

Price Paid: _____

Market Value: _____

Purchased At: _____

Moderate

Easy

STRUT
the Rooster

BEANIE BABIES
Series II
4171
1999

BEANIE BABIES OFFICIAL CLUB™
STRUT
the Rooster
Birthday: 3-8-96
Issued: 7-12-97
Listen closely to
"cock-a-doodle-doo"
What's the rooster
saying to you?
Hurry, wake up
sleepy head
We have lots to do,
get out of bed!
231
4171

LITTLE-KNOWN FACTS:
The Rooster is the tenth
sign of the Chinese
Horoscope. People born
under the sign of the
Rooster are said to be
resilient, enthusiastic
and have a good sense
of humor.

©1999 TY INC. BEANIE BABIES OFFICIAL CLUB

Card #
232

Tabasco • 4002

TABASCO
the Bull

BEANIE BABIES
Series II
4002
1999

Moderate

Easy

BEANIE BABIES OFFICIAL CLUB™
TABASCO
the Bull
Birthday: 5-15-95
Issued: 6-3-95
Although Tabasco
is not so tall
He loves to play
basketball
He is a star player
in his dream
Can you guess
his favorite team?
232
4002

LITTLE-KNOWN FACTS:
Bulls are from the family
Bovidae and the species
Taurus. Taurus is also an
astrological sign. Most
Tauruses are said to be
strong-minded and very
independent. You are a
Taurus if born between
April 20 and May 19.

©1999 TY INC. BEANIE BABIES OFFICIAL CLUB

Date Purchased: _____

Price Paid: _____

Market Value: _____

Purchased At: _____

COMMON CARDS

141

1st Edition

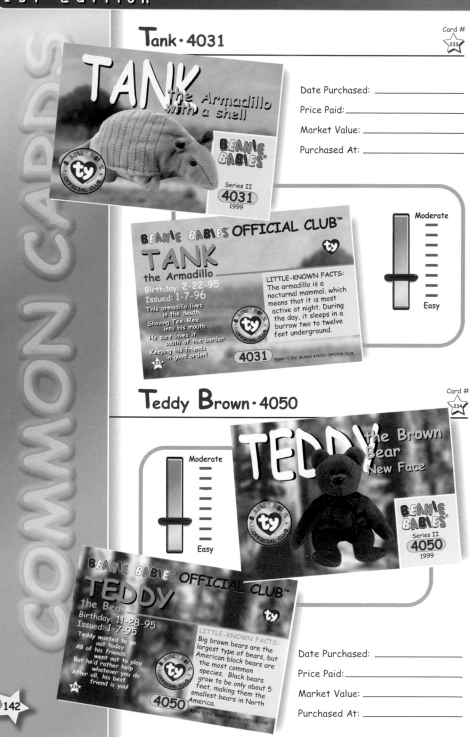

Tank · 4031

Date Purchased: _____

Price Paid: _____

Market Value: _____

Purchased At: _____

TANK the Armadillo with a shell

BEANIE BABIES
Series II
4031
1999

BEANIE BABIES OFFICIAL CLUB™
TANK
the Armadillo
Birthday: 2-22-95
Issued: 1-7-96
This armadillo lives
in the South
Shoving Tex-Mex
into his mouth
He sure loves it
south of the border
Keeping his friends
in good order!

LITTLE-KNOWN FACTS:
The armadillo is a
nocturnal mammal, which
means that it is most
active at night. During
the day, it sleeps in a
burrow two to twelve
feet underground.

4031 ©1999 TY INC. BEANIE BABIES OFFICIAL CLUB

Moderate — Easy

Teddy Brown · 4050

Moderate — Easy

TEDDY the Brown Bear New Face

BEANIE BABIES
Series II
4050
1999

BEANIE BABIES OFFICIAL CLUB™
TEDDY
the Bear
Birthday: 11-28-95
Issued: 1-7-95
Teddy wanted to go
out today
All of his friends
went out to play
But he'd rather help
whatever you do
After all, his best
friend is you!

LITTLE-KNOWN FACTS:
Big brown bears are the
largest type of bears, but
American black bears are
the most common
species. Black bears
grow to be only about 5
feet, making them the
smallest bears in North
America.

4050 ©1999 TY INC. BEANIE BABIES OFFICIAL CLUB

Date Purchased: _____

Price Paid: _____

Market Value: _____

Purchased At: _____

COMMON CARDS

Teddy Brown • 4050

Card #
235

Date Purchased: _____

Price Paid: _____

Market Value: _____

Purchased At: _____

TEDDY the Brown Bear Old Face

BEANIE BABIES Series II
4050
1999

Moderate
Easy

BEANIE BABIES OFFICIAL CLUB™

TEDDY the Bear

Birthday: Unknown
Issued: 6-25-94

Teddy wanted to go
out today
All of his friends
went out to play
But he'd rather help
whatever you do
After all, his best
friend is you!

LITTLE-KNOWN FACTS:
Grizzly bears can grow up
to 8 feet long and weigh a
whopping 350-500 lbs.!
They get that name from
the white hairs that pop
up between their brown
hairs, making them look
grizzled.

4050

©1999 TY INC. BEANIE BABIES OFFICIAL CLUB

Teddy Cranberry • 4052

Card #
236

TEDDY the Cranberry Bear Old Face

BEANIE BABIES Series II
4052
1999

Moderate
Easy

BEANIE BABIES OFFICIAL CLUB™

TEDDY the Bear

Birthday: Unknown
Issued: 6-25-94

LITTLE-KNOWN FACTS:
Zoologists recognize
seven different species
of bears, including big
brown bears, American
black bears, Asiatic
black bears, polar
bears, sun bears, sloth
bears, and spectacled
bears.

4052

©1999 TY INC. BEANIE BABIES OFFICIAL CLUB

Date Purchased: _____

Price Paid: _____

Market Value: _____

Purchased At: _____

143

COMMON CARDS

1st Edition

COMMON CARDS

Teddy Jade · 4057

Card #
237

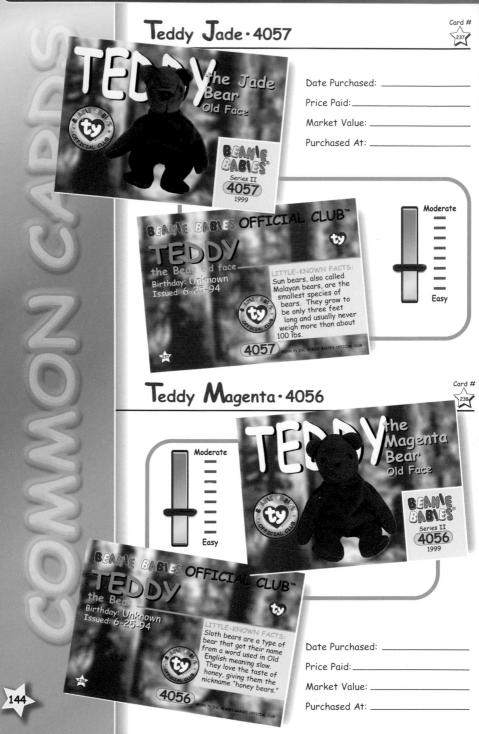

TEDDY the Jade Bear Old Face

BEANIE BABIES
Series II
4057
1999

Date Purchased: _____

Price Paid: _____

Market Value: _____

Purchased At: _____

BEANIE BABIES OFFICIAL CLUB™

TEDDY the Bear old face

Birthday: Unknown
Issued: 6-25-94

LITTLE-KNOWN FACTS:
Sun bears, also called Malayan bears, are the smallest species of bears. They grow to be only three feet long and usually never weigh more than about 100 lbs.

4057

Moderate

Easy

Teddy Magenta · 4056

Card #
238

Moderate

Easy

TEDDY the Magenta Bear Old Face

BEANIE BABIES
Series II
4056
1999

BEANIE BABIES OFFICIAL CLUB™

TEDDY the Bear

Birthday: Unknown
Issued: 6-25-94

LITTLE-KNOWN FACTS:
Sloth bears are a type of bear that got their name from a word used in Old English meaning slow. They love the taste of honey, giving them the nickname "honey bears."

4056

Date Purchased: _____

Price Paid: _____

Market Value: _____

Purchased At: _____

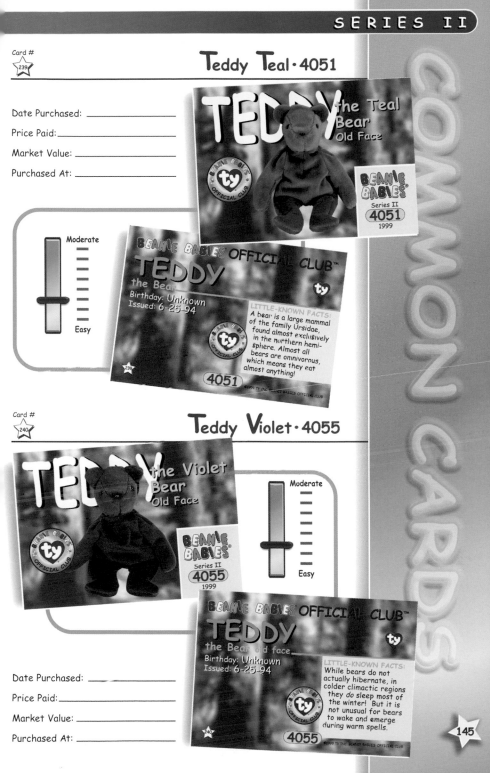

Card #
239

Teddy Teal • 4051

Date Purchased: _____

Price Paid: _____

Market Value: _____

Purchased At: _____

Moderate

Easy

TEDDY
the Teal Bear
Old Face

BEANIE BABIES
Series II
4051
1999

BEANIE BABIES OFFICIAL CLUB

TEDDY
the Bear
Birthday: Unknown
Issued: 6-25-94

LITTLE-KNOWN FACTS:
A bear is a large mammal of the family Ursidae, found almost exclusively in the northern hemisphere. Almost all bears are omnivorous, which means they eat almost anything!

4051

Card #
240

Teddy Violet • 4055

TEDDY
the Violet Bear
Old Face

BEANIE BABIES
Series II
4055
1999

Moderate

Easy

BEANIE BABIES OFFICIAL CLUB

TEDDY
the Bear old face
Birthday: Unknown
Issued: 6-25-94

LITTLE-KNOWN FACTS:
While bears do not actually hibernate, in colder climactic regions they do sleep most of the winter! But it is not unusual for bears to wake and emerge during warm spells.

4055

©1999 TY INC. BEANIE BABIES OFFICIAL CLUB

Date Purchased: _____

Price Paid: _____

Market Value: _____

Purchased At: _____

COMMON CARDS

145

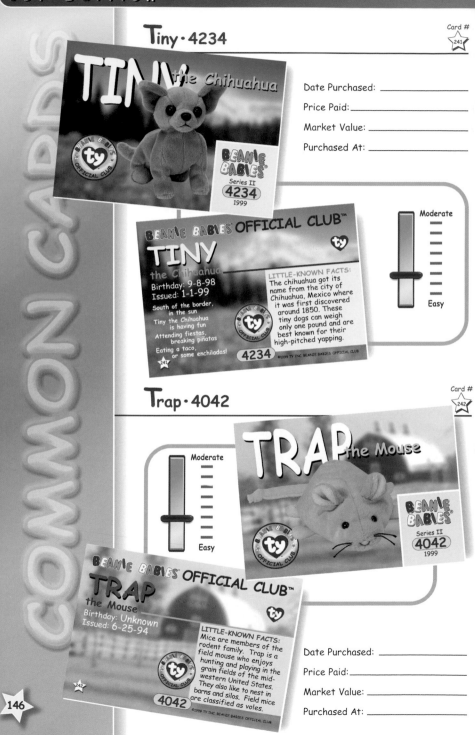

Tiny • 4234

Card #
241

Date Purchased: _____

Price Paid: _____

Market Value: _____

Purchased At: _____

TINY the Chihuahua

ty
BEANIE BABIES
Series II
4234
1999

BEANIE BABIES OFFICIAL CLUB™

TINY
the Chihuahua

ty

Birthday: 9-8-98
Issued: 1-1-99

South of the border,
in the sun
Tiny the Chihuahua
is having fun
Attending fiestas,
breaking piñatas
Eating a taco,
or some enchiladas!

LITTLE-KNOWN FACTS:
The chihuahua got its
name from the city of
Chihuahua, Mexico where
it was first discovered
around 1850. These
tiny dogs can weigh
only one pound and are
best known for their
high-pitched yapping.

4234
©1999 TY INC. BEANIE BABIES OFFICIAL CLUB

Moderate
Easy

Trap • 4042

Card #
242

Moderate
Easy

TRAP the Mouse

BEANIE BABIES
Series II
4042
1999

BEANIE BABIES OFFICIAL CLUB™

TRAP
the Mouse

ty

Birthday: Unknown
Issued: 6-25-94

LITTLE-KNOWN FACTS:
Mice are members of the
rodent family. Trap is a
field mouse who enjoys
hunting and playing in the
grain fields of the mid-
western United States.
They also like to nest in
barns and silos. Field mice
are classified as voles.

4042
©1999 TY INC. BEANIE BABIES OFFICIAL CLUB

Date Purchased: _____

Price Paid: _____

Market Value: _____

Purchased At: _____

COMMON CARDS

Card #
244

Valentina • 4233

Date Purchased: _____

Price Paid: _____

Market Value: _____

Purchased At: _____

Moderate

Easy

VALENTINA
the Bear

BEAMIE BABIES OFFICIAL CLUB™

VALENTINA
the Bear
Birthday: 2-14-98
Issued: 1-1-99

Flowers, candy
and hearts galore
Sweet words of love
for those you adore
With the bear comes
love that's true
On Valentine's Day
and all year through!

LITTLE-KNOWN FACTS:
Valentine's Day falls on
February 14, the feast day of
St. Valentine. It is often cele-
brated by sending greetings,
in the form of "valentines,"
that express affection or
friendship to sweethearts,
friends and family.

4233

©1999 TY INC. BEANIE BABIES OFFICIAL CLUB

Card #
245

Web • 4041

WEB
the Spider

BEAMIE BABIES
Series II
4041
1999

Moderate

Easy

BEAMIE BABIES OFFICIAL CLUB™

WEB
the Spider
Birthday: UNKNOWN
Issued: 6-25-94

LITTLE-KNOWN FACTS:
Spiders can spin many
types of webs. Young
spiders spin a parachute
web, which the wind can
catch and carry for
miles. Others spin a
more complex web,
using it to catch food,
especially flying insects.

4041

©1999 TY INC. BEANIE BABIES OFFICIAL CLUB

Date Purchased: _____

Price Paid: _____

Market Value: _____

Purchased At: _____

147

COMMON CARDS

1st Edition

Wise · 4187

WISE the Owl

CLASS OF '98

BEANIE BABIES
Series II
4187
1999

BEANIE BABIES OFFICIAL CLUB™

Wise
the Owl

Birthday: 5-31-97
Issued: 5-30-98

With A's and B's
he'll always pass
Wise is the head
of the class
He's got his diploma
and feels really great
Meet the newest graduate:
Class of 98!

LITTLE-KNOWN FACTS:
Many owls have their ear
openings at different
levels on either side of
their head. This allows
them to better judge
the position and dis-
tance of their target,
but it can sure make for
some funny-looking owls!

4187

©1999 TY INC. BEANIE BABIES OFFICIAL CLUB

Moderate — Easy

Date Purchased: _____

Price Paid: _____

Market Value: _____

Purchased At: _____

Zero · 4207

ZERO the Penguin

BEANIE BABIES
Series II
4207
1999

Moderate — Easy

BEANIE BABIES OFFICIAL CLUB™

ZERO
the Penguin

Birthday: 1-2-98
Issued: 9-30-98

Penguins love the
ice and snow
Playing in weather
twenty below
Antarctica is where
I love to be
Splashing in the
cold, cold sea!

LITTLE-KNOWN FACTS:
Penguins have water-
resistant feathers and a
thick layer of fat to help
protect them against the
cold. Their small
extremities also help
keep heat inside their
bodies. Zero also wears a
hat for extra protection!

4207

©1999 TY INC. BEANIE BABIES OFFICIAL CLUB

Date Purchased: _____

Price Paid: _____

Market Value: _____

Purchased At: _____

COMMON CARDS

Card #
248

Zip • 4004

Date Purchased: _____

Price Paid: _____

Market Value: _____

Purchased At: _____

ZIP the Black Cat

BEANIE BABIES

Series II
4004
1999

Moderate

Easy

BEANIE BABIES OFFICIAL CLUB™

ZIP
the Cat

Birthday: 3-28-94
Issued. 1-7-96

Keep Zip by your side
all the day through
Zip is good luck,
you'll see it's true
When you have something
you need to do
Zip will always
believe in you!

4004

LITTLE-KNOWN FACTS:
Cats were worshipped in
ancient Egypt because
they helped control the
rat population. These
felines of the Nile
were held in such high
regard that it was
forbidden to take cats
out of the country!

©1999 TY INC. BEANIE BABIES OFFICIAL CLUB

Card #
249

Zip • 4004

ZIP the Cat
with white paws

BEANIE BABIES

Series II
4004
1999

Moderate

Easy

BEANIE BABIES OFFICIAL CLUB™

ZIP
the Cat

Birthday: 3-28-94
Issued: 3-10-96

Keep Zip by your side
all the day through
Zip is good luck,
you'll see it's true
When you have something
you need to do
Zip will always
believe in you!

4004

LITTLE-KNOWN FACTS:
A cat's whiskers act as
little fingers, helping it
feel its way around in
the dark and through
tight spaces. These
whiskers, known as
"vibrissae," are a unique
and important part of
the cat's anatomy.

©1999 TY INC. BEANIE BABIES OFFICIAL CLUB

Date Purchased: _____

Price Paid: _____

Market Value: _____

Purchased At: _____

COMMON CARDS

149

BIRTHDAY CARDS

The Birthday/Rookie Cards

The first of the chaser card subsets in Series II, the Birthday/Rookie cards are similar to those found in Series I, but with a few key design changes that make them unique. Each Series II Birthday/Rookie card has been formatted vertically rather than horizontally, so that they look tall rather than wide. The front of each card is in full color and shows a Beanie, its name, its birthday, the series number, and the Official Club logo. Some of the cards in this category are stamped "ROOKIE". These cards represent Beanies that were part of the "new release" of Beanies that came out after the appearance of Series I cards.

The image of the Beanie lies on a background of detailed etched foil. The name of each Birthday Beanie has been foil stamped below it in one of four glossy colors: bright blue, light green, silver, and gold. The color of the embossed name determines the level of rarity of that particular card. The easiest variation to find in this subgroup is blue, then green, silver, and finally, the most difficult variation to find, gold. Each gold card is crash-numbered 1 of a limited amount, adding another level of collectibility.

The back of each card shows the Beanie's birth date, issue date, style number, This Day in History, and their poem. There are 24 Birthday/Rookie cards in Series II, numbered 250 to 273. The odds of finding a Birthday/Rookie card are 1 in 3 packs.

BIRTHDAY CARDS

Card #
250

Baldy • 4074

BEANIE BABIES
HAPPY 2-17 1996 BIRTHDAY
BALDY
the Eagle
250
Series 2
4074
1999

Difficult

GOLD

SILVER
GREEN
BLUE
Moderate

BALDY
the Eagle
Birthday: 2-17-96
Issued: 5-11-97

Hair on his head is quite scant
We suggest Baldy get a transplant
Watching over the land of the free
Hair in his eyes would make it hard to see!

ON THIS DAY IN HISTORY
On February 17, 1817 the first gas-lit streetlights were illuminated on the streets of Baltimore, Maryland.

AUTHENTIC ty PRODUCT
©1999 TY INC BEANIE BABIES OFFICIAL CLUB
Series 2
4074
1999
BEANIE BABIES

	B	Gr	S	G
Date Purchased:				
Price Paid:				
Market Value:				
Purchased At:				

Card #
251

Beak • 4211

BEANIE BABIES
HAPPY 2-3 1998 BIRTHDAY
ROOKIE
BEAK
the Kiwi Bird
251
Series 2
4211
1999

Difficult

GOLD

SILVER
GREEN
BLUE
Moderate

BEAK
the Kiwi Bird
Birthday: 2-3-98
Issued: 9-30-98

Isn't this just the funniest bird?
When we saw her, we said "how absurd"
Looks aren't everything, this we know
Her love for you, she's sure to show!

ON THIS DAY IN HISTORY
Beak the Kiwi Bird shares a birthday with famous artist Norman Rockwell, who was born on February 3, 1894. Rockwell is famous for his cover art for The Saturday Evening Post.

AUTHENTIC ty PRODUCT
©1999 TY INC. BEANIE BABIES OFFICIAL CLUB
Series 2
4211
1999
BEANIE BABIES

	B	Gr	S	G
Date Purchased:				
Price Paid:				
Market Value:				
Purchased At:				

1st Edition

Caw · 4071

Card #
252

BEANIE BABIES
BIRTHDAY UNKNOWN
252
CAW
the Crow
Series 2
4071
1999

Difficult
GOLD
SILVER
GREEN
BLUE
Moderate

CAW
the Crow
Birthday: UNKNOWN   Issued: 6-3-95

ON THIS DAY IN HISTORY
On June 3, 1851 the baseball
team known as the New York
Knickerbockers became the first
baseball team to wear uniforms during
a game. The players were white
shirts, blue pants and straw hats!

AUTHENTIC ty PRODUCT
©1999 TY INC. BEANIE BABIES OFFICIAL CLUB
Series 2
4071
1999
BEANIE BABIES

	B	Gr	S	G
Date Purchased:				
Price Paid:				
Market Value:				
Purchased At:				

Early · 4190

Card #
253

BEANIE BABIES
HAPPY 3-20 1997 BIRTHDAY
253
EARLY
the Robin
4190
1999

Difficult
GOLD
SILVER
GREEN
BLUE
Moderate

EARLY
the Robin
Early is a
red breasted robin
For a worm he'll soon
be a-bobbin'
Always known
as a sign of spring
This happy robin
loves to sing!
Birthday: 3-20-97
Issued: 5-30-98

ON THIS DAY IN HISTORY
On March 20, 1914 in New
Haven, Connecticut, the first
international figure skating
championship was held!

AUTHENTIC ty PRODUCT
©1999 TY INC. BEANIE BABIES OFFICIAL CLUB
Series 2
4190
1999
BEANIE BABIES

	B	Gr	S	G
Date Purchased:				
Price Paid:				
Market Value:				
Purchased At:				

BIRTHDAY CARDS

BIRTHDAY CARDS

Card #
254

Echo • 4180

BEANIE BABIES
HAPPY 12-21 1996 BIRTHDAY

ECHO
the Dolphin
254   4180
1999

Difficult
GOLD
SILVER
GREEN
BLUE
Moderate

ECHO
the Dolphin
Echo the dolphin
lives in the sea
Playing with her friends
like you and me
Through the waves
she echos the sound
"I'm so glad
to have you around!"

Birthday: 12-21-96
Issued: 5-11-97

ON THIS DAY IN HISTORY
On December 21, 1966 the
famous band The Beach Boys
were awarded a gold record for
the hit single, "Good Vibrations."

AUTHENTIC ty PRODUCT
©1999 TY INC BEANIE BABIES OFFICIAL CLUB
4180
1999
BEANIE BABIES

	B	Gr	S	G
Date Purchased:				
Price Paid:				
Market Value:				
Purchased At:				

Card #
255

Fleece • 4125

BEANIE BABIES
HAPPY 3-21 1996 BIRTHDAY

FLEECE
the Napped Lamb
255   4125
1999

Difficult
GOLD
SILVER
GREEN
BLUE
Moderate

FLEECE
the Napped Lamb
Fleece would like to
sing a lullaby
But please be patient,
she's rather shy
When you sleep
keep her by your ear
Her song will leave you
nothing to fear.

Birthday: 3-21-96
Issued: 1-1-97

ON THIS DAY IN HISTORY
Fleece the Napped Lamb
shares a birthday with the
great composer Johann
Sebastian Bach, who was born
on March 21, 1685.

AUTHENTIC ty PRODUCT
©1999 TY INC BEANIE BABIES OFFICIAL CLUB
4125
1999
BEANIE BABIES

	B	Gr	S	G
Date Purchased:				
Price Paid:				
Market Value:				
Purchased At:				

153

1st Edition

Freckles • 4066

Card #
256

BEANIE BABIES
HAPPY 6-3 1996 BIRTHDAY

FRECKLES
the Leopard
256
Series 2
4066
1999

FRECKLES
the Leopard

From the trees
he hunts prey.
In the night
and in the day
He's the king
of camouflage.
Look real close,
he's no mirage!

Birthday: 6-3-96
Issued: 6-15-96

ON THIS DAY IN HISTORY
On June 3, 1800 John Adams
became the first President to
live in what became the U.S capital,
Washington, DC. After five months
he moved into The People's House,
later renamed the White House.

AUTHENTIC ty PRODUCT
©1999 TY INC. BEANIE BABIES OFFICIAL CLUB
Series 2
4066
1999

BEANIE BABIES

	B	Gr	S	G
Date Purchased:				
Price Paid:				
Market Value:				
Purchased At:				

Gigi • 4191

Card #
257

BEANIE BABIES
HAPPY 4-7 1997 BIRTHDAY

GIGI
the Poodle
257
Series 2
4191
1999

GIGI
the Poodle

Prancing and dancing
all down the street
Thinking her hairdo
is oh so neat
Always so careful
in the wind and rain
She's a dog that is
anything but plain!

Birthday: 4-7-97
Issued: 5-30-98

ON THIS DAY IN HISTORY
On April 7, 1992 the USA and
the European Community recogniz-
ed the independence of Croatia,
Slovenia, Bosnia and Hercegovina
from the former Yugoslavia.

AUTHENTIC ty PRODUCT
©1999 TY INC. BEANIE BABIES OFFICIAL CLUB
Series 2
4191
1999

BEANIE BABIES

	B	Gr	S	G
Date Purchased:				
Price Paid:				
Market Value:				
Purchased At:				

BIRTHDAY CARDS

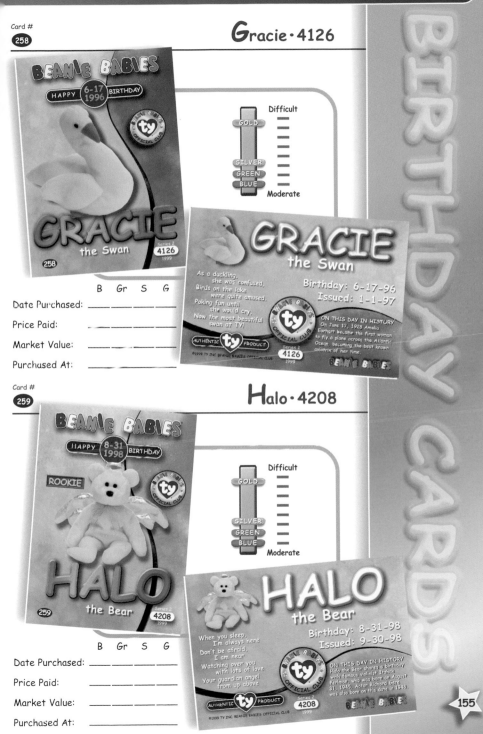

Card #
258

Gracie • 4126

BEANIE BABIES

HAPPY 6-17 1996 BIRTHDAY

GRACIE
the Swan
258
Series 2
4126
1999

Difficult

GOLD

SILVER
GREEN
BLUE

Moderate

GRACIE
the Swan

As a duckling,
she was confused,
Birds on the lake
were quite amused,
Poking fun until
she would cry,
Now the most beautiful
Swan at TY!

Birthday: 6-17-96
Issued: 1-1-97

AUTHENTIC ty PRODUCT

Series 2
4126
1999

ON THIS DAY IN HISTORY
On June 17, 1928 Amelia
Earhart became the first woman
to fly a plane across the Atlantic
Ocean, becoming the best known
aviatrix of her time.

©1999 TY INC. BEANIE BABIES OFFICIAL CLUB

BEANIE BABIES

	B	Gr	S	G
Date Purchased:				
Price Paid:				
Market Value:				
Purchased At:				

Card #
259

Halo • 4208

BEANIE BABIES

HAPPY 8-31 1998 BIRTHDAY

ROOKIE

HALO
the Bear
259
Series 2
4208
1999

Difficult

GOLD

SILVER
GREEN
BLUE

Moderate

HALO
the Bear

When you sleep,
I'm always here
Don't be afraid,
I am near
Watching over you
with lots of love
Your guardian angel
from up above

Birthday: 8-31-98
Issued: 9-30-98

AUTHENTIC ty PRODUCT

Series 2
4208
1999

ON THIS DAY IN HISTORY
Halo the Bear shares a birthday
with famous violinist Itzhak
Perlman, who was born on August
31, 1945. Actor Richard Gere
was also born on this date in 1948.

©1999 TY INC. BEANIE BABIES OFFICIAL CLUB

BEANIE BABIES

	B	Gr	S	G
Date Purchased:				
Price Paid:				
Market Value:				
Purchased At:				

155

Hissy · 4185

Card # 260

Difficult

GOLD

SILVER
GREEN
BLUE

Moderate

HISSY
The Snake
Birthday: 4-4-97
Issued: 12-31-97

Curled and coiled
and ready to play
He waits for you patiently
every day
He'll keep his best friend,
but not his skin
And stay with you
through thick and thin!

AUTHENTIC **ty** PRODUCT
©1999 TY INC. BEANIE BABIES OFFICIAL CLUB

BEANIE & THE
ty
OFFICIAL CLUB

ON THIS DAY IN HISTORY
On April 4, 1887, Susanna M.
Salter became the first woman
mayor of a United States city.
That city was Argonia, Kansas.

Series 2
4185
1999

BEANIE BABIES

BEANIE BABIES
HAPPY 4-4 1997 BIRTHDAY

HISSY
the Snake

260

Series 2
4185
1999

	B	Gr	S	G
Date Purchased:				
Price Paid:				
Market Value:				
Purchased At:				

Jabber · 4197

Card # 261

Difficult

GOLD

SILVER
GREEN
BLUE

Moderate

JABBER
the Parrot
Birthday: 10-10-97
Issued: 5-30-98

Teaching Jabber
to move his beak
A large vocabulary
he now can speak
Jabber will repeat
what you say
Teach him a new word
every day!

AUTHENTIC **ty** PRODUCT
©1999 TY INC. BEANIE BABIES OFFICIAL CLUB

BEANIE & THE
ty
OFFICIAL CLUB

ON THIS DAY IN HISTORY
On October 10, 1913 the largest
construction project in history was
finally completed. The digging of the
Panama Canal connected the Atlantic
and Pacific oceans.

Series 2
4197
1999

BEANIE BABIES

BEANIE BABIES
HAPPY 10-10 1997 BIRTHDAY

JABBER
the Parrot

261

Series 2
4197
1999

	B	Gr	S	G
Date Purchased:				
Price Paid:				
Market Value:				
Purchased At:				

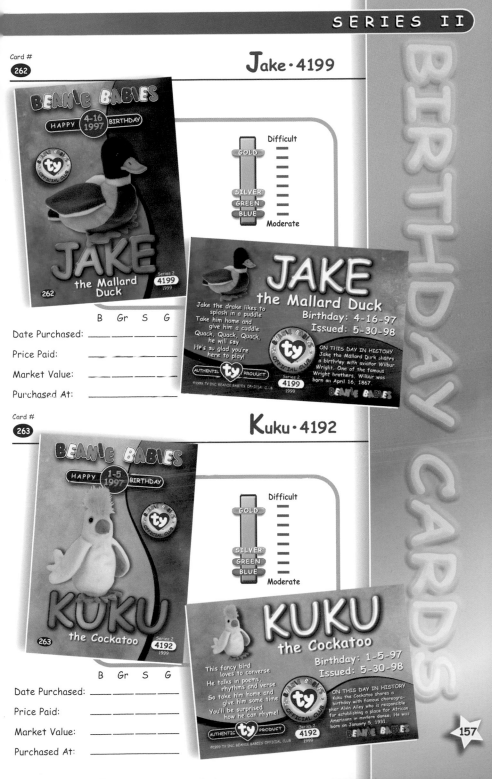

Card #
262

Jake · 4199

BEANIE BABIES
HAPPY 4-16 1997 BIRTHDAY

JAKE
the Mallard Duck
Series 2
4199
1999
262

Difficult
GOLD
SILVER
GREEN
BLUE
Moderate

JAKE
the Mallard Duck
Jake the drake likes to
splash in a puddle
Take him home and
give him a cuddle
Quack, Quack, Quack,
he will say
He's su glad you're
here to play!

AUTHENTIC ty PRODUCT
©1999 TY INC. BEANIE BABIES OFFICIAL CLUB
Series 2
4199
1999

Birthday: 4-16-97
Issued: 5-30-98

ON THIS DAY IN HISTORY
Jake the Mallard Duck shares
a birthday with aviator Wilbur
Wright. One of the famous
Wright brothers, Wilbur was
born on April 16, 1867.

BEANIE BABIES

B Gr S G

Date Purchased: _____

Price Paid: _____

Market Value: _____

Purchased At: _____

Card #
263

Kuku · 4192

BEANIE BABIES
HAPPY 1-5 1997 BIRTHDAY

KUKU
the Cockatoo
Series 2
4192
1999
263

Difficult
GOLD
SILVER
GREEN
BLUE
Moderate

KUKU
the Cockatoo
This fancy bird
loves to converse
He talks in poems,
rhythms and verse
So take him home and
give him some time
You'll be surprised
how he can rhyme!

AUTHENTIC ty PRODUCT
©1999 TY INC. BEANIE BABIES OFFICIAL CLUB
Series 2
4192
1999

Birthday: 1-5-97
Issued: 5-30-98

ON THIS DAY IN HISTORY
Kuku the Cockatoo shares a
birthday with famous choreogra-
pher Alvin Ailey who is responsible
for establishing a place for African
Americans in modern dance. He was
born on January 5, 1931.

BEANIE BABIES

B Gr S G

Date Purchased: _____

Price Paid: _____

Market Value: _____

Purchased At: _____

BIRTHDAY CARDS

BIRTHDAY CARDS

1st Edition

Nip · 4003

Card # 264

Difficult

GOLD

SILVER
GREEN
BLUE

Moderate

BEANIE BABIES

HAPPY 3-6 1994 BIRTHDAY

NIP
the Gold Cat

264

Series 2
4003
1999

NIP
The Gold Cat

His name is Nipper,
but we call him Nip
His best friend is
a black cat named Zip.
Nip likes to run
in races for fun
He runs so fast he's
always number one!

Birthday: 3-6-94
Issued: 1-7-96

ON THIS DAY IN HISTORY
Nip shares a birthday with great
Renaissance artist Michelangelo, who
painted the ceiling of the Sistine
Chapel and sculpted the famous work
of David. Michelangelo was born on
March 6, 1475.

AUTHENTIC ty PRODUCT

©1999 TY INC. BEANIE BABIES OFFICIAL CLUB

Series 2
4003
1999

BEANIE BABIES

	B	Gr	S	G
Date Purchased:				
Price Paid:				
Market Value:				
Purchased At:				

Nuts · 4114

Card # 265

Difficult

GOLD

SILVER
GREEN
BLUE

Moderate

BEANIE BABIES

HAPPY 1-21 1996 BIRTHDAY

NUTS
the Squirrel

265

Series 2
4114
1999

NUTS
the Squirrel

With his bushy tail, he'll
scamper up a tree.
The most cheerful critter
you'll ever see.
He's nuts about nuts,
and he loves to chat
Have you ever seen
a squirrel like that?

Birthday: 1-21-96
Issued: 1-1-97

ON THIS DAY IN HISTORY
The first opera ever heard over
a national radio network was
presented in Chicago on January
21, 1927. Selections from Faust
were broadcast.

AUTHENTIC ty PRODUCT

©1999 TY INC. BEANIE BABIES OFFICIAL CLUB

Series 2
4114
1999

BEANIE BABIES

	B	Gr	S	G
Date Purchased:				
Price Paid:				
Market Value:				
Purchased At:				

Patti · 4025

Card #
266

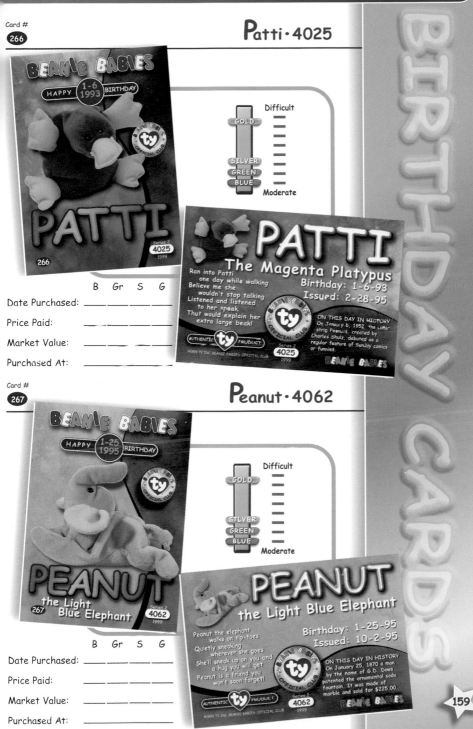

Date Purchased: _____

Price Paid: _____

Market Value: _____

Purchased At: _____

Card #
267

Peanut · 4062

Date Purchased: _____

Price Paid: _____

Market Value: _____

Purchased At: _____

BIRTHDAY CARDS

1st Edition

Pumkin · 4205

Card #
268

Difficult

GOLD
SILVER
GREEN
BLUE

Moderate

BEANIE BABIES
HAPPY 10-31 1998 BIRTHDAY
ROOKIE
PUMKIN
the Pumpkin
268
Series 2
4205
1999

PUMKIN
the Pumpkin

Ghost and goblins are
out tonight
Witches try hard to
cause fright
This little pumkin is
very sweet
He only wants to trick
or treat!

Birthday: 10-31-98
Issued: 9-30-98

ON THIS DAY IN HISTORY
Pumkin the Pumpkin shares a
birthday with renowned poet John
Keats, who was born on October
31, 1795. Keats poems are still
widely read and studied today.

AUTHENTIC ty PRODUCT
©1999 TY INC. BEANIE BABIES OFFICIAL CLUB

Series 2
4205
1999

BEANIE BABIES

	B	Gr	S	G
Date Purchased:				
Price Paid:				
Market Value:				
Purchased At:				

Rainbow · 4037

Card #
269

Difficult

GOLD
SILVER
GREEN
BLUE

Moderate

BEANIE BABIES
HAPPY 10-14 1997 BIRTHDAY

RAINBOW
the Chameleon
269
Series 2
4037
1999

RAINBOW
the Chameleon

Red, green, blue,
and yellow
This chameleon is
a colorful fellow
A blend of colors,
his own unique hue
Rainbow was made
especially for you!

Birthday: 10-14-97
Issued: 12-31-97

ON THIS DAY IN HISTORY
Rainbow the Chameleon shares
his birthday with Dwight D.
Eisenhower, the 34th President of
the United States, who was born
on October 14, 1890 in Denison,
Texas.

AUTHENTIC ty PRODUCT
©1999 TY INC. BEANIE BABIES OFFICIAL CLUB

Series 2
4037
1999

BEANIE BABIES

	B	Gr	S	G
Date Purchased:				
Price Paid:				
Market Value:				
Purchased At:				

BIRTHDAY CARDS

Rocket • 4202

Date Purchased: _____

Price Paid: _____

Market Value: _____

Purchased At: _____

B   Gr   S   G

ROCKET
the Blue Jay

Rocket is the fastest
blue jay ever
He flies in all
sorts of weather
Aerial tricks are
his specialty
He's so entertaining
for you and me!

Birthday: 3-12-97
Issued: 5-30-98

ON THIS DAY IN HISTORY
On March 12, 1933, President
Franklin Delano Roosevelt
presented his first presidential
address to the nation. It was the
first of what were known as
Roosevelt's famous Fireside Chats.

Rover • 4101

ROVER
the Dog

Birthday: 5-30-96
Issued: 6-15-96

This dog is red and
his name is Rover
If you call him he is
sure to come over
He barks and plays
with all his might
But worry not,
he won't bite!

ON THIS DAY IN HISTORY
On May 30, 1922 the Lincoln
Memorial was dedicated in the
United States capital of
Washington, DC.

Date Purchased: _____

Price Paid: _____

Market Value: _____

Purchased At: _____

B   Gr   S   G

161

BIRTHDAY CARDS

Smoochy • 4039

Card # 272

Difficult

GOLD

SILVER
GREEN
BLUE

Moderate

SMOOCHY
The Frog

Is he a frog
or maybe a prince?
This confusion
makes him wince
Find the answer,
help him with this
Be the one to give
him a kiss!

Birthday: 10-1-97
Issued: 12-31-97

ON THIS DAY IN HISTORY
Smoochy the Frog shares a
birthday with Jimmy Carter,
the 39th President of the
United States, who was born on
October 1, 1924 in Plains, GA.

AUTHENTIC ty PRODUCT
©1999 TY INC. BEANIE BABIES OFFICIAL CLUB

Series 2
4039
1999

BEANIE BABIES

	B	Gr	S	G
Date Purchased:				
Price Paid:				
Market Value:				
Purchased At:				

Snip • 4120

Card # 273

Difficult

GOLD

SILVER
GREEN
BLUE

Moderate

SNIP
the Siamese Cat

Snip the cat
is Siamese
She'll be your friend
if you please
So toss her a toy
or a piece of string
Playing with you is
her favorite thing!

Birthday: 10-22-96
Issued: 1-1-97

ON THIS DAY IN HISTORY
On October 22, 1797, the
world's first known parachute
jump was made from a hot-air
balloon in Paris, France. The
jumper was André-Jacques
Garnerin.

AUTHENTIC ty PRODUCT
©1999 TY INC. BEANIE BABIES OFFICIAL CLUB

Series 2
4120
1999

BEANIE BABIES

	B	Gr	S	G
Date Purchased:				
Price Paid:				
Market Value:				
Purchased At:				

The Retired Cards

The Retired cards in Series II showcase a variety of retired Beanies not seen in Series I. The quality and originality of the cards in this card subset reflects their level of rarity. Again, you can expect to see some exciting design changes from the Series I Retired cards.

Like the Birthday/Rookie cards, these Series II cards are designed on a vertical format rather than a horizontal one. The front of each Retired card shows a Beanie, its name, retired date, and series number. Dimension is created by designing with both black and white and four-color artwork overprinting the holographic board stock. When the card is shifted about under light, a flashing prism of colors can be seen.

The name of each Beanie is debossed. The retired date is embossed and foil stamped in one of four colors. As with the Birthday cards, the color of this embossed stamp determines the level of rarity of the card. The same four levels of color are used here: blue, green, silver, and gold, with the easiest variation to find being blue, and the most difficult, gold. Each gold card is crash-numbered 1 of a limited amount, adding another level of collectibility.

There are 15 Retired cards in Series II, numbered 274 to 288. The odds of finding a Retired card are 1 in 5 packs.

RETIRED CARDS

RETIRED CARDS

Ally • 4032

274

	B	Gr	S	G
Date Purchased:				
Price Paid:				
Market Value:				
Purchased At:				

Ally
the alligator

10-1 RETIRED 97

274

Ally
the alligator

Birthday: 3-14-94
Issued: 6-25-94
Retired: 10-1-97

When Ally gets
out of classes
He wears a hat and
dark glasses
He plays bass in
a street band
He's the coolest gator
in the land!

Style No. 4032

©1999 TY INC BEANIE BABIES OFFICIAL CLUB

Difficult

GOLD

SILVER
GREEN
BLUE

Moderate

Bumble • 4045

275

	B	Gr	S	G
Date Purchased:				
Price Paid:				
Market Value:				
Purchased At:				

Bumble
the bee

Bumble
the bee

Birthday: Unknown
Issued: 6-3-95
Retired: 6-15-96

Bumble the bee will
not sting you
It is only love that this
bee will bring you.
So don't be afraid to
give this bee a hug
Because Bumble the
Bee is a lovebug.

6-15 RETIRED 96

275

Style No. 4045

©1999 TY INC BEANIE BABIES OFFICIAL CLUB

Difficult

GOLD

SILVER
GREEN
BLUE

Moderate

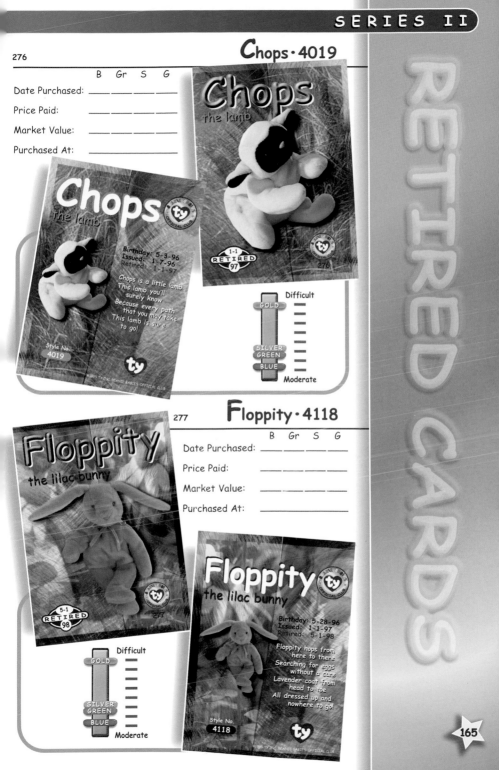

Chops · 4019

276

	B	Gr	S	G
Date Purchased:				
Price Paid:				
Market Value:				
Purchased At:				

Chops
the lamb

Birthday: 5-3-96
Issued: 1-7-96
Retired: 1-1-97

Chops is a little lamb
This lamb you'll
surely know
Because every path
that you may take
This lamb is sure
to go!

Style No.
4019

Chops
the lamb

1-1
RETIRED
97

276

Difficult
GOLD
SILVER
GREEN
BLUE
Moderate

Floppity · 4118

277

	B	Gr	S	G
Date Purchased:				
Price Paid:				
Market Value:				
Purchased At:				

Floppity
the lilac bunny

5-1
RETIRED
98

277

Difficult
GOLD
SILVER
GREEN
BLUE
Moderate

Floppity
the lilac bunny

Birthday: 5-28-96
Issued: 1-1-97
Retired: 5-1-98

Floppity hops from
here to there
Searching for eggs
without a care
Lavender coat from
head to toe
All dressed up and
nowhere to go!

Style No.
4118

Grunt · 4092

278

	B	Gr	S	G
Date Purchased:				
Price Paid:				
Market Value:				
Purchased At:				

Difficult

GOLD

SILVER
GREEN
BLUE

Moderate

Grunt
the razorback

Birthday: 7-19-95
Issued: 1-7-96
Retired: 5-11-97

Some Beanies think
Grunt is tough
No surprise, he's
scary enough
But if you take him
home you'll see
Grunt is the sweetest
Beanie Baby!

Style No.
4092

©1999 TY INC BEANIE BABIES OFFICIAL CLUB

5-11 RETIRED 97

Jolly · 4082

279

	B	Gr	S	G
Date Purchased:				
Price Paid:				
Market Value:				
Purchased At:				

Jolly
the walrus

Birthday: 12-2-96
Issued: 5-11-97
Retired: 5-1-98

Jolly the walrus is
not very serious
He laughs and
laughs until he's
delirious
He often reminds
me of my dad
Always happy,
never sad!

Style No.
4082

©1999 TY BEANIE BABIES OFFICIAL CLUB

5-1 RETIRED 98

Difficult

GOLD

SILVER
GREEN
BLUE

Moderate

RETIRED CARDS

Lizzy · 4033

280

	B	Gr	S	G
Date Purchased:				
Price Paid:				
Market Value:				
Purchased At:				

Lizzy
the blue lizard

Birthday: 12-2-96
Issued: 5-11-97
Retired: 5-1-98

Lizzy loves Legs
the frog.
She hides with him
under logs.
Both of them
search for flies
Underneath the
clear blue skies!

Style No.
4033

©1999 TY INC. BEANIE BABIES OFFICIAL CLUB

12-31
RETIRED
97

280

Difficult

GOLD

SILVER
GREEN

BLUE

Moderate

Lucky · 4040

281

	B	Gr	S	G
Date Purchased:				
Price Paid:				
Market Value:				
Purchased At:				

Lucky
the ladybug

2-27
RETIRED
96

281

Lucky
the ladybug

Birthday: 5-1-95
Issued: 6-25-94
Retired: 2-27-96

Lucky the ladybug
loves the lotto
"Someone must win"
that's her motto
But save your dimes
and even a penny
Don't spend on the
lotto and you'll
have many!

Style No
4040

Difficult

GOLD

SILVER
GREEN

BLUE

Moderate

RETIRED CARDS

Magic · 4088

282

	B	Gr	S	G
Date Purchased:				
Price Paid:				
Market Value:				
Purchased At:				

Magic
the dragon!

12-31 RETIRED 97

282

Magic
the dragon

Birthday: 9-5-95
Issued: 6-3-95
Retired: 12-31-97

Magic the dragon
lives in a dream
The most beautiful
that you have
ever seen
Through magic lands
she likes to fly
Look up and watch
her, way up high!

Style No.
4088

Difficult
GOLD
SILVER
GREEN
BLUE
Moderate

Puffer · 4181

283

	B	Gr	S	G
Date Purchased:				
Price Paid:				
Market Value:				
Purchased At:				

Puffer
the puffin

9-18 RETIRED 98

283

Puffer
the puffin

Birthday: 11-3-97
Issued: 12-31-97
Retired: 9-18-98

What in the world
does a puffin do?
We're sure that you
would like to
know too
We asked Puffer
how she spends
her days
Before she answered,
she flew away!

Style No.
4181

Difficult
GOLD
SILVER
GREEN
BLUE
Moderate

RETIRED CARDS

168

284

Rex • 4086

	B	Gr	S	G
Date Purchased:				
Price Paid:				
Market Value:				
Purchased At:				

Rex
the tyrannosaurus

Rex
the tyrannosaurus

Birthday: Unknown
Issued: 6-3-95
Retired: 6-15-96

6-15
RETIRED
96

284

Style No.
4086

ty

©1999 TY INC. BEANIE BABIES OFFICIAL CLUB

Difficult

GOLD

SILVER
GREEN
BLUE

Moderate

285

Seaweed • 4080

	B	Gr	S	G
Date Purchased:				
Price Paid:				
Market Value:				
Purchased At:				

Seaweed
the otter

9-19
RETIRED
98

285

Difficult

GOLD

SILVER
GREEN
BLUE

Moderate

Seaweed
the otter

Birthday: 3-19-96
Issued: 1-7-96
Retired: 9-19-98

Seaweed is what she
likes to eat
It's supposed to be a
delicious treat
Have you tried a
treat from
the water
If you haven't,
maybe you 'otter'!

Style No.
4080

ty

©1999 TY INC. BEANIE BABIES OFFICIAL CLUB

RETIRED CARDS

RETIRED CARDS

Sly • 4115

286

	B	Gr	S	G
Date Purchased:				
Price Paid:				
Market Value:				
Purchased At:				

Sly
the brown
bellied fox

8-6 RETIRED 96

286

Sly
the brown bellied fox

Birthday: 9-12-96
Issued: 6-15-96
Retired: 8-6-96

Sly is a fox and
tricky is he.
Please don't chase
him, let him be
If you want him
just say when
He'll peek out from
his den!

Style No.
4115

©1999 TY INC. BEANIE BABIES OFFICIAL CLUB

Difficult

GOLD

SILVER
GREEN
BLUE

Moderate

Snort • 4002

287

	B	Gr	S	G
Date Purchased:				
Price Paid:				
Market Value:				
Purchased At:				

Snort
the bull

9-15 RETIRED 98

287

Snort
the bull

Birthday: 5-15-95
Issued: 1-1-97
Retired: 9-15-98

Although Snort is
not so tall
He loves to play
basketball
He is a star player
in his dream
Can you guess his
favorite team?

Style No.
4002

©1999 TY INC. BEANIE BABIES OFFICIAL CLUB

Difficult

GOLD

SILVER
GREEN
BLUE

Moderate

Twigs • 4068

B   Gr   S   G

Date Purchased: ___ ___ ___ ___

Price Paid: ___ ___ ___ ___

Market Value: ___ ___ ___ ___

Purchased At: ___

Twigs
the giraffe

Birthday: 5-19-95
Issued: 1-7-96
Retired: 4-30-98

Twigs has his head
in the clouds
He stands tall, he
stands proud
With legs so skinny
they wobble
and shake
What an unusual
friend he
will make!

Style No.
4068

RETIRED 4-30 98

Difficult

GOLD

SILVER
GREEN
BLUE

Moderate

The Rare Bear Cards

The last and most rare subset in Series II are the Rare Bear cards. The cards in this category feature some of the most collectible Beanie Babies Bears made by Ty.

The design of the Rare Bear cards is as unique and rare in the trading card world as the bears themselves! Rare Bear cards are created from original stereogram holograms that produce an image that is rich in both color and depth. These cards are best viewed under natural or halogen light. Turn the card and watch the bear change!

The front of each Rare Bear card shows the bear with its name and left chest emblem printed across the bottom of the card. Below the name, each card has been foil stamped for authenticity with the words "the bear" in one of the four color variations for Series II: blue, green, silver, or gold. As with the other subsets, the easiest variation to find is blue, and the most difficult, gold. Each Rare Bear card is crash-numbered 1 of a limited amount, making them very rare indeed!

There are 12 Rare Bear cards representing card numbers 289 to 300, and the odds of finding a Rare Bear card are 1 in 50 packs.

#1 Bear

	B	Gr	S	G
Date Purchased:				
Price Paid:				
Market Value:				
Purchased At:				

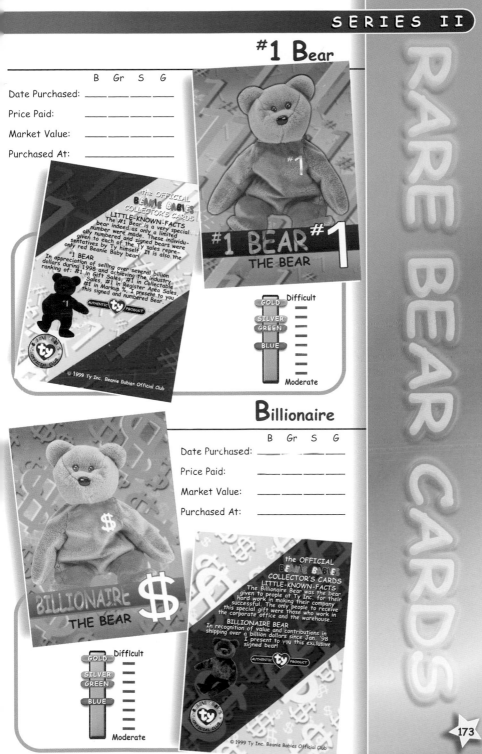

the OFFICIAL
BEANIE BABIES
COLLECTOR'S CARDS
LITTLE-KNOWN-FACTS
The #1 Bear is a very special
bear indeed as only a limited
number were made. These individually numbered and signed bears were
given to each of the Ty sales repre-
sentatives by Ty himself. It is also the
only red Beanie Baby bear!

#1 BEAR
In appreciation of selling over several billion
dollars during 1998 and achieving the industry
ranking of: #1 in Gift Sales, #1 in Collectable
Sales, #1 in Register Area Sales,
#1 in Markup, I present to you
this signed and numbered Bear.

AUTHENTIC ty PRODUCT

© 1999 Ty Inc. Beanie Babies Official Club

#1 BEAR #1
THE BEAR

GOLD — Difficult
SILVER
GREEN
BLUE
Moderate

Billionaire

	B	Gr	S	G
Date Purchased:				
Price Paid:				
Market Value:				
Purchased At:				

BILLIONAIRE $
THE BEAR

GOLD — Difficult
SILVER
GREEN
BLUE
Moderate

the OFFICIAL
BEANIE BABIES
COLLECTOR'S CARDS
LITTLE-KNOWN-FACTS
The Billionaire Bear was the bear
given to people at Ty Inc. for their
hard work in making their company
successful. The only people to receive
this special gift were those who work in
the corporate office and the warehouse.

BILLIONAIRE BEAR
In recognition of value and contributions in
shipping over a billion dollars since Jan. '98
I present to you this exclusive
signed bear!

AUTHENTIC ty PRODUCT

© 1999 Ty Inc. Beanie Babies Official Club

RARE BEAR CARDS

Britannia · 4601

	B	Gr	S	G
Date Purchased:				
Price Paid:				
Market Value:				
Purchased At:				

the OFFICIAL
BEANIE BABIES
COLLECTOR'S CARDS

LITTLE-KNOWN-FACTS
Britannia the Bear wears the
British flag, or "Union Jack"
with pride. Britannia is the first
Beanie Baby ever made which is distrib-
uted exclusively in the United Kingdom.

BRITANNIA THE BEAR
Britannia the bear will sail the sea
So she can be with you and me
She's always sure to catch the tide
And wear the Union Flag with pride!

AUTHENTIC ty PRODUCT

4601

© 1999 Ty Inc. Beanie Babies Official Club

GOLD — Difficult
SILVER
GREEN
BLUE

Moderate

Clubby

	B	Gr	S	G
Date Purchased:				
Price Paid:				
Market Value:				
Purchased At:				

the OFFICIAL
BEANIE BABIES
COLLECTOR'S CARDS

LITTLE-KNOWN-FACTS
Clubby the Bear always wears
his Official Club button. He is the
exclusive Beanie Baby available only
to Charter Members of the Beanie
Babies Official Club. Look for other
special offers for 'members only!

CLUBBY THE BEAR
Wearing his club pin for all to see
He's a proud member like you and me
Made especially with you in mind
Clubby the Bear is one of a kind!

AUTHENTIC ty PRODUCT

© 1999 Ty Inc. Beanie Babies Official Club

GOLD — Difficult
SILVER
GREEN
BLUE

Moderate

RARE BEAR CARDS

Erin · 4186

	B	Gr	S	G
Date Purchased:				
Price Paid:				
Market Value:				
Purchased At:				

the OFFICIAL
BEANIE BABIES
COLLECTOR'S CARDS
LITTLE-KNOWN-FACTS
An ambassador of Ireland, Erin the Bear wears a lucky four leaf clover. Fortunately for us, Erin can be found worldwide, not just in Ireland — sharing the luck of the Irish with all who are lucky to find her!

ERIN THE BEAR
Named after the beautiful Emerald Isle This Beanie Baby will make you smile. A bit of luck, a pot of gold, Light up the faces, both young and old!

AUTHENTIC ty PRODUCT
4186

© 1999 Ty Inc. Beanie Babies Official Club

ERIN
THE BEAR

Difficult
GOLD
SILVER
GREEN
BLUE
Moderate

Garcia · 4051

	B	Gr	S	G
Date Purchased:				
Price Paid:				
Market Value:				
Purchased At:				

GARCIA
THE BEAR

GARCIA
the bear

Difficult
GOLD
SILVER
GREEN
BLUE
Moderate

the OFFICIAL
BEANIE BABIES
COLLECTOR'S CARDS
LITTLE-KNOWN-FACTS
A rainbow of colors, Garcia the Bear is the first Ty-dye Beanie Bear! It is said that Garcia was named after a legendary musician whose fans followed him around the country and around the globe. Do you know his name?

GARCIA THE BEAR
The Beanies used to follow him around Because Garcia traveled from town to town He's pretty popular as you can see Some even say he's legendary!

AUTHENTIC ty PRODUCT
4051

© 1999 Ty Inc. Beanie Babies Official Club

RARE BEAR CARDS

RARE BEAR CARDS

Glory · 4188

	B	Gr	S	G
Date Purchased:				
Price Paid:				
Market Value:				
Purchased At:				

GLORY
THE BEAR

the OFFICIAL
BEANIE BABIES
COLLECTOR'S CARDS

LITTLE-KNOWN-FACTS
This star-spangled Beanie Baby
proudly wears the American flag,
but he is available worldwide. Glory
is the only Beanie™ bear wearing a
flag that is not exclusive to that
specific country.

GLORY THE BEAR
Wearing the flag for all to see
Symbol of freedom for you and me
Red white and blue-Independence Day
Happy Birthday USA !

AUTHENTIC ty PRODUCT
4188

© 1999 Ty Inc. Beanie Babies Official Club

GOLD — Difficult
SILVER
GREEN
BLUE
Moderate

Libearty · 4057

	B	Gr	S	G
Date Purchased:				
Price Paid:				
Market Value:				
Purchased At:				

the OFFICIAL
BEANIE BABIES
COLLECTOR'S CARDS

LITTLE-KNOWN-FACTS
Like his friend Glory, Libearty
the Bear is honored to wear the
American Flag. Libearty can only be
found in the United States, and was
the first Beanie™ created exclusively for
its home country.

LIBEARTY THE BEAR
I am called Libearty,
I wear the flag for all to see
Hope and freedom is my way
That's why I wear flag USA!

AUTHENTIC ty PRODUCT
4057

© 1999 Ty Inc. Beanie Babies Official Club

LIBEARTY
THE BEAR

GOLD — Difficult
SILVER
GREEN
BLUE
Moderate

176

RARE BEAR CARDS

Maple • 4600

	B	Gr	S	G
Date Purchased:				
Price Paid:				
Market Value:				
Purchased At:				

the OFFICIAL
BEANIE BABIES
COLLECTOR'S CARDS
LITTLE-KNOWN-FACTS
Maple the Bear is adorned with
the Canadian Flag, and is exclu-
sively distributed in Canada. The
Canadian flag features a red maple
leaf with eleven points, and was
adopted by the country in 1965.

MAPLE THE BEAR
Maple the Bear likes to ski
With his friends he plays hockey
He loves his pancakes and
eats every crumb
Can you guess what country
he's from?

AUTHENTIC ty PRODUCT

4600

© 1999 Ty Inc. Beanie Babies Official Club

MAPLE
THE BEAR

CANADA

GOLD — Difficult
SILVER
GREEN
BLUE
Moderate

Peace • 4053

	B	Gr	S	G
Date Purchased:				
Price Paid:				
Market Value:				
Purchased At:				

PEACE
THE BEAR

the OFFICIAL
BEANIE BABIES
COLLECTOR'S CARDS
LITTLE-KNOWN-FACTS
Peace the Bear is collectable for
many reasons, primarily because no
two are alike! Peace was made in
three different color variations of
Ty-Dye — bright colors, neon colors
and pastels.

PEACE THE BEAR
All races, all colors, under the sun
Join hands together and have some fun
Dance to the music, rock and roll
is the sound
Symbols of peace
and love abound!

AUTHENTIC ty PRODUCT

4053

© 1999 Ty Inc. Beanie Babies Official Club

GOLD — Difficult
SILVER
GREEN
BLUE
Moderate

RARE BEAR CARDS

Princess • 4300

	B	Gr	S	G
Date Purchased:				
Price Paid:				
Market Value:				
Purchased At:				

PRINCESS
THE BEAR

GOLD — Difficult
SILVER
GREEN
BLUE
Moderate

the OFFICIAL
BEANIE BABIES
COLLECTOR'S CARDS

LITTLE-KNOWN-FACTS
The proceeds of Princess the Bear are donated to the Diana, Princess of Wales Memorial Fund. Between her issue date in 1997 and the end of 1998, this little bear raised over 10 million dollars!

PRINCESS THE BEAR
Like an angel she came from heaven above. She shared her compassion, her pain, her love. She only stayed with us long enough to teach. The world to share, to give, to reach.

AUTHENTIC ty PRODUCT

4300

© 1999 Ty Inc. Beanie Babies Official Club

Valentino • 4058

	B	Gr	S	G
Date Purchased:				
Price Paid:				
Market Value:				
Purchased At:				

the OFFICIAL
BEANIE BABIES
COLLECTOR'S CARDS

LITTLE-KNOWN-FACTS
Valentino the Bear wears his heart on his chest. Although Valentino is special because he was born on Valentine's Day, he is also special because he was the first Beanie Buby to wear an embroidered crest.

VALENTINO THE BEAR
His heart is red and full of love. He cares for you so give him a hug. Keep him close when feeling blue. Feel the love he has for you!

AUTHENTIC ty PRODUCT

4058

© 1999 Ty Inc. Beanie Babies Official Club

VALENTINO
THE BEAR

GOLD — Difficult
SILVER
GREEN
BLUE
Moderate

It pays to be part of the Club!

These limited edition Platinum Series cards can be purchased only as part of the Beanie Babies Official Club Kit — Platinum Edition. Each Club Kit contains one package of three different cards which are unlike any of the cards previously available in the 1st Edition Series I and Series II. These Platinum Edition cards feature three exciting new card styles that you won't find anywhere else, with five different Beanies featured in each style. Because the total set of cards is made up of 15 different cards of equal distribution, you can count on getting one of each style in every pack!

Talk about hidden treasure! These unique Platinum Series card styles include:

• Mosaic cards, which have embossed accents and a foil stripe that surrounds the featured Beanie's name.

• Nature cards, which depict each Beanie highlighted on an abstract background with a photo of its natural habitat.

• Double Emboss cards, which display each Beanie's name in bold, embossed relief.

Club membership definitely has its rewards!

PLATINUM CARDS

Bronty • 4085

Date Purchased: _____

Price Paid: _____

Purchased At: _____

Market Value: _____

Legs • 4020

Date Purchased: _____

Price Paid: _____

Purchased At: _____

Market Value: _____

Millenium • 4226

Date Purchased: _____

Price Paid: _____

Purchased At: _____

Market Value: _____

Signature • 4228

Date Purchased: _____

Price Paid: _____

Purchased At: _____

Market Value: _____

Steg • 4087

Date Purchased: _____

Price Paid: _____

Purchased At: _____

Market Value: _____

PLATINUM CARDS

PLATINUM CARDS

Beak · 4211

Date Purchased: _____

Price Paid: _____

Purchased At: _____

Market Value: _____

Echo · 4180

Date Purchased: _____

Price Paid: _____

Purchased At: _____

Market Value: _____

Goldie · 4023

Date Purchased: _____

Price Paid: _____

Purchased At: _____

Market Value: _____

Jabber · 4197

Date Purchased: _____

Price Paid: _____

Purchased At: _____

Market Value: _____

Rex · 4086

Date Purchased: _____

Price Paid: _____

Purchased At: _____

Market Value: _____

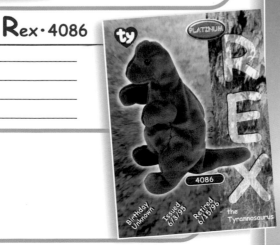

PLATINUM CARDS

PLATINUM CARDS

Bessie • 4009

Date Purchased: _____

Price Paid: _____

Purchased At: _____

Market Value: _____

Clubby

Date Purchased: _____

Price Paid: _____

Purchased At: _____

Market Value: _____

Peanut • 4062

Date Purchased: _____

Price Paid: _____

Purchased At: _____

Market Value: _____

Princess • 4300

Date Purchased: _____

Price Paid: _____

Purchased At: _____

Market Value: _____

Quackers • 4024

Date Purchased: _____

Price Paid: _____

Purchased At: _____

Market Value: _____

PLATINUM CARDS

These authentic Ty products are now available at your favorite retail Beanie Babies® Official Club™ Headquarters!

Official Collector's Cards

* 1ˢᵗ Edition, Series I and II, total 300 separate Collector's Cards
* Beautifully printed and finished with embossing and foil stamping
* Nine cards per pack plus a checklist

Ty-Lite Storage Box

* Colorful Collector's Card Box for storage and display of Official Beanie Babies® Collector's Cards
* Exclusive design stores cards with or without individual card protectors
* Front locking clasp for closing and safekeeping

Beanie Babies® Display Case

* Protects and safeguards individual Beanie Babies® against dust and harmful UV rays
* Transparent plastic design allows viewing from all angles
* Selection of colorful environmental backgrounds to display your Beanies
* Interlocking embossed Ty heart on top and bottom for easy stacking

AUTHENTIC ty PRODUCT

Official BBOC Platinum Membership Kit

* Exclusive new BBOC Beanie Baby®, Clubby II
* Platinum Edition Set of Beanie Babies®
  Collector's Cards
* One Platinum Edition Collector's Coin
* Platinum Edition Membership Card
* Platinum Edition Certificate
  of Membership
* Beanie Babies Official Club Newsletter
* Official 1999 Beanie Babies
  Pocket Checklist
* All in a reusable, durable travel case

Official Collector's Cards Display Album

* 3-ring binder with inside
  storage pockets
* 5 pages of protective sleeves
* Exclusive Authentic Ty®
  Product Foil Stamp appears
  on each page
* Holds nine cards per page
* Acid free, archival safe
  polypropylene
* Additional Protective Pages
  available (sold separately)

Individual Collector's Cards Protectors

* Protects and safeguards each of your valuable
  Beanie Babies® Collector's Cards
* Transparent, rigid PVC prevents bending or
  creasing of cards
* Archival safe, acid free, protects from
  harmful UV rays

BEANIE BABIES®
Official Millennium Calendar

* Sixteen-month official calendar
* Beanie™ photos in vibrant, glossy
  full color featuring an international celebration of Beanies
  from around the world
* Beanie™ birthdays and international fun facts

Frequently Asked Questions

There's a real buzz about Beanie Babies Official Collector's Cards — they're generating lots of excitement and loads of questions! We've tried to answer some of those questions in order to ensure that the information you have is accurate and current. We may even answer a few questions you didn't know you had!

Series I:

Are all of the Beanies represented in Series I?
No. Every Beanie is not represented in the Series I. There are 149 different Beanies in Series I, all of which are listed on the checklist included in every pack.

How can I collect them all?
We do not guarantee that you will be able to collect the entire set. Just like Beanies, some are easier to find than others. The odds are likely that an entire set of Common cards will be found within a Masterpack of Collector's Cards (a Masterpack is made up of 6 counter displays), but again, there are no guarantees! Many retailers are sponsoring "Trading Days", where they invite customers to trade their Official Beanie Babies Collector's Cards with one another, no cash involved. This helps to create more excitement about the game of trading, while allowing card fans to fill holes in their collections.

Did Ty Warner really sign some of the cards?
Yes! Ty Warner has personally autographed one of every card in Series I. Each of these signed cards is also numbered 1/1 to show that they are one-of-a-kind.

I didn't get all nine cards in my pack. How could this happen?
Because of strict quality control measures, chances of this happening are slim. The cards are collated into their foil packs in an automated process designed to guarantee their collation frequency. After the packs are sealed, they are weighed. If a pack is over the proper weight, indicating that it could hold an extra card, it continues to be packed in a box. Any packs that are light, or potentially short of a card, are removed from the process and checked later for proper card count. Because the weight of the different types of cards varies slightly, a pack might on rare occasions pass with a missing card.

If I purchase a dealer or counter display box, how do I know that it hasn't been opened already?
A Dealer or Counter Display Box holds 24 packs of cards. These boxes are packaged with an all-over plastic seal designed to protect against tampering. Check to see that this plastic seal has not been removed or torn before purchasing.

I am a retailer and I received a colorful sliding card with my counter display box. What is this for?
This is just a fun "dealer loader", also known in trading card circles as a "schmeggie" or free gift. Anyone who purchased the dealer box, which contains 24 packs of Collector's Cards, received this slider card as a thank you for supporting the introductory series of Beanie Babies Official Collector's Cards. If you pull down

the tab at the bottom of the slider, the black and white picture shown will change to color! There are eight different slider cards, each with a different picture.

Series II:

Are all of the beanies represented in Series II?
No, every Beanie is not represented in the second series. There are 151 Beanies in Series II, all of which are listed on the checklist included in every pack.

Are there duplicate cards between Series I and Series II?
There are no exact duplicates, however, you may see some familiar faces. For example, Derby the Horse with a White Star was featured as a Common card in Series I, and the original Derby the Horse is featured as a Common card in Series II. Splash the Whale appeared in Series I as one of the Original 9 Chaser cards, and appears in Series II as a Common card.

Why are the Common cards the same in Series I and Series II?
The Common cards in the 1st Edition are all created with the same embossed style with the scenic background, so they share the same look and feel. They are consecutively numbered 50 to 149 in Series I, and continue with 150 to 249 in Series II.

Why do some of the Birthday Beanie cards say "Rookie" on them?
Some of the cards in the Birthday/Rookie category are stamped "ROOKIE". These cards represent Beanies that were part of the "new release" of Beanies that came out after the appearance of Series I cards. They are called Rookies because they are relatively new on the Beanie scene!

How can I collect them all?
Like with Series I, we do not guarantee that you will be able to collect the entire set. The odds are likely that an entire set of Common cards will be found within a Masterpack of Collector's Cards (a Masterpack is made up of 6 counter displays), but again, there are no guarantees!

What are the scratch cards in each pack?
In place of the mini-puzzle card that appeared in every pack in Series I, we've put a trivia game card in every pack in Series II. There are 25 different scratch-off trivia game cards in the series, collated in equal distribution, which means that you have an equal chance of getting any one of the 25 cards. Use the cards to test your Beanie trivia knowledge by yourself, or with a friend!

I am a retailer and I received a colorful poster with my dealer or counter display box. What is this for?
This is just a fun "dealer loader", also known in trading card circles as a "schmeggie" or "box-topper". Anyone who purchased the dealer box, which contains 24 packs of Collector's Cards, received this poster as part of Series II of the Beanie Babies Official Collector's Cards. The front of the poster shows each of the 149 cards featured in Series I, while the back features the 151 cards from Series II.

1st Edition

Glossary of Trading Card Terms

Box-Topper: A free gift not found in regularly purchased packs of cards, also known as a "schmeggie". The box-topper is usually included only with boxed cards (multiple packs of usually 24, 36, or 48 packages of cards). The box-topper is intended to be an added bonus for retailers and consumers who buy cards by the box.

Card Stock: The thickness and type of cardboard used to make a card. Referred to in points, the higher the number of points, the thicker the card. The thicker cards are generally more expensive. The average card is 16 to 20 points, with 24 points being a very thick, and therefore more expensive card.

Case: Cards pre-packaged by the case are sometimes made available by manufacturers. Usually 6 to 20 wax boxes are in a case of cards. Dealers sometimes buy cards by the case and receive special cards as part of the purchase.

Case Card: A special card that comes only with the purchase of a case of cards. Usually this special card is a rare chase card or card that can only be found in a case. The Case Card is an incentive for dealers to buy cards by the case. Case Cards are not always offered.

Chaser Card: Chaser cards are special cards that are not part of the standard set of Common cards. Chaser cards are usually more difficult to find as they are produced in smaller amounts than the Common cards, and are randomly inserted into packs. Chaser cards are usually of a higher quality than the Common cards.

Common Cards: The standard cards that make up the majority of a set.

Crash-numbered: Cards that are crash-numbered are individually numbered 1 of a limited amount. For example, a card numbered 1/1 is a one-of-a-kind card. A card numbered 1/50 is number 1 in a series of 50 total numbered cards.

Embossed Cards: Cards that have been pressed as part of the design/production process, resulting in a raised or textured surface.

Excellent Condition: Standard trading card term — see page 13.

Fair Condition: Standard trading card term — see page 14.

Foil Card: Cards that have been designed with a metallic foil affixed or etched onto their surface.

Good Condition: Standard trading card term — see page 14.

HoloChrome Cards: Cards that have both a chrome design on them, and a hologram design. Usually Chaser cards.

HoloFoil Cards: Cards that have both a foil design on them, and a hologram design. Usually Chaser cards.

Hologram Cards: These cards are usually silver or gold, and have been designed with laser technology to have a three-dimensional appearance when viewed in the right light. Usually Chaser cards.

Mint Condition: Standard trading card term — see page 13.

Near Mint Condition: Standard trading card term — see page 13.

Page: A soft, clear plastic page that fits into a binder that is used to display and protect trading cards. The clear plastic allows the collector to see both the front and back of their cards.

Poor: Standard trading card term — see page 14.

Prizmatic Foil Cards: Cards that have been designed with a process that produces a rainbow-like effect on the card. Usually a Chaser card.

Refractor Cards: These are Chromium cards that have been designed to produce an additional rainbow-like effect when held at an angle under the right light.

Schmeggie: (see also "Box-Topper")

Sleeve: A soft or rigid plastic pocket that holds one card for protection and display.

Spectra Cards: Foil cards that have had the foil area etched to produce greater detail.

Uncut Sheet: Production term for a sheet of cards before they are cut into individual cards.

Very Good Condition: Standard trading card term — see page 13.

Wax: The term used for cards that are still in their original packaging.

Wax Box: The term for the box that packages of cards come in. There are usually 24, 36, or 48 packages of cards to a box.

Wax Pack: The term for the individual packs that cards come in. There are usually four to ten cards in a pack. The term "Wax Pack" comes from the 60's and 70's when packages of trading cards were made from wax paper. Today, these same packages are usually made from plastic or foil.

OFFICIAL GUIDE TO BEANIE BABIES COLLECTOR'S CARDS

INDEX